GETTING THE
MOST FROM
YOUR
MULTIMETER

OTHER TITLES OF INTEREST

BP70	Transistor Radio Fault Finding Chart
BP101	How to Identify Unmarked ICs
BP110	How to Get Your Electronic Projects Working
BP120	Audio Amplifier Fault Finding Chart
BP248	Test Equipment Construction
BP265	More Advanced Uses of the Multimeter
BP267	How to Use Oscilloscopes and Other Test Equipment

GETTING THE MOST FROM YOUR MULTIMETER

by
R. A. PENFOLD

BERNARD BABANI (publishing) LTD
THE GRAMPIANS
SHEPHERDS BUSH ROAD
LONDON W6 7NF
ENGLAND

PLEASE NOTE

Although every care has been taken with the production of this book to ensure that any projects, designs, modifications and/or programs etc. contained herewith, operate in a correct and safe manner and also that any components specified are normally available in Great Britain, the Publishers do not accept responsibility in any way for the failure, including fault in design, of any project, design, modification or program to work correctly or to cause damage to any other equipment that it may be connected to or used in conjunction with, or in respect of any other damage or injury that may be so caused, nor do the Publishers accept responsibility in any way for the failure to obtain specified components.

Notice is also given that if equipment that is still under warranty is modified in any way or used or connected with home-built equipment then that warranty may be void.

© 1988 BERNARD BABANI (publishing) LTD

First Published — April 1988
Reprinted — June 1989
Reprinted — April 1990

British Library Cataloguing in Publication Data
Penfold, R. A.
    Getting the most from your multimeter.
    1. Electronics equipment. Testing with
       multimeter-Manuals
    I. Title
    621.3815'48

ISBN 0 85934 184 4

Printed and Bound in Great Britain by Cox & Wyman Ltd, Reading

Preface

A multimeter is probably the first item of test equipment that most electronics enthusiasts purchase, and over the years it has remained the most useful piece of test gear available at moderate cost. It would be an exaggeration to say that a multimeter is all that is needed in order to test any item of home constructed electronics, but a multimeter is all that is needed for most day-to-day testing. Having other pieces of test equipment available can certainly speed up the checking process in many cases, but a multimeter and some thoughtful checking will suffice in the vast majority of situations. However, like any piece of test equipment, a multimeter is of little use unless you understand how it can be put to effective use, and are aware of its limitations.

This book is primarily aimed at beginners and those of limited experience of electronics. Chapter 1 covers the basics of analogue and digital multimeters, discussing the relative merits and the limitations of the two types. In Chapter 2 various methods of component checking are described, including tests for transistors, thyristors, resistors, capacitors, and diodes. Circuit testing is covered in Chapter 3, with subjects such as voltage, current, and continuity checks being discussed. In the main little or no previous knowledge or experience is assumed. Using these simple component and circuit testing techniques the reader should be able to confidently tackle servicing of most home constructed electronic projects.

R. A. Penfold

Contents

Page

Chapter 1
CHOOSING A MULTIMETER 1
Analogue or Digital 1
A.C. Voltage 7
Decibels 8
D.C. Current 11
Analogue Resistance 13
Other Features 14
Digital Multimeters 17
A.C. Voltage 21
Current 22
Linear Resistance 23
Semi Digits 25
Extras 26
Which Type? 27

Chapter 2
COMPONENT TESTING 31
Resistors 31
Potentiometers 35
Thermistors and Cds Cells 37
Capacitance 38
Value Gauging 40
Diodes and Rectifiers 41
Zener Diodes 44
Transistors 45
Improved Tester 51
VMOS 51
Power MOSFETs 56
SCRs 59
LEDs 61
Photo-Transistors 62
Loudspeakers 62
Transformers and Inductors 63
Batteries 63
Switches 64
Finally 66

Chapter 3
   CIRCUIT TESTING 67
      Initial Tests 67
      Continuity Testing 69
      Mains Equipment 71
      Divided Voltages 76
      Estimating Voltages 77
      No Change 80
      Bias Voltage 81
      Current Tracing 82
      Which Fault? 83
      Oscillators 84
      Response Limitations 89
      R.F. Oscillators 91
      Audio Measurements 95
      Logic Testing 98

Chapter 1

CHOOSING A MULTIMETER

I suppose it is true to say that for an electronics enthusiast any multimeter is infinitely better than no multimeter at all. On the other hand, some instruments are very much more capable than others. It is very much a matter of getting what you pay for, and expensive types generally have higher specifications and better build quality than the cheaper models. As with most technical products, more money pays for more features, but a point is soon reached where a marginally higher specification means a great deal more cost. The most cost effective instruments tend to be the ones that have a fairly full specification, and not the ones that suffer from the laws of diminishing returns!

Analogue or Digital

There are two distinct categories of multimeter in the form of digital and analogue instruments. The latter tend to be considered as second best to the former, but this is really an over-simplistic attitude. Digital multimeters certainly have higher specifications than analogue multimeters in certain important respects, but they do have one or two disadvantages as well. Superficially the only difference between the two types is that one has a digital display while the other has an analogue readout (which invariably means a moving coil meter). There are other and equally substantial differences though.

In this chapter we will take a detailed look at both forms of multimeter, the basics of how they function, and the advantages and drawbacks of each type. This is not all of purely academic importance. An understanding of multimeter basics is needed when choosing the best instrument to suit your needs (and budget), and also when using the instrument. When a multimeter is connected to a test circuit its effect on the circuit must not be ignored. What is apparently a fault could just be an erroneous reading caused by loading or other effects of the multimeter on the test circuit.

If we consider analogue instruments first, these do not normally include any active electronics. In the past there were actually several different electronic analogue multimeters on sale, but these have been effectively replaced by digital multimeters, and no longer seem to be available. The fact that an analogue multimeter lacks any active electronics is not purely of academic importance. It means that the energy to drive the meter movement must be provided by the test circuit, and the meter must be a sensitive type if the instrument is to give usable results.

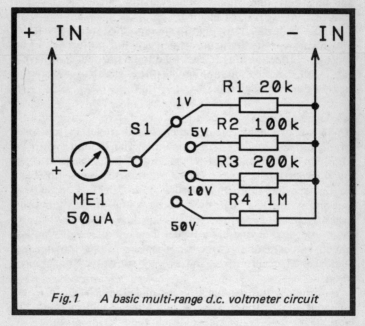

Fig.1   A basic multi-range d.c. voltmeter circuit

The problem is one of loading, and the basic multimeter circuit of Figure 1 helps to explain what can happen if the meter lacks sensitivity. Here we have a 50 microamp meter with four switched series resistors of 20k, 100k, 200k, and 1M. If you apply Ohm's Law to these resistances you will find that potentials of 1, 5, 10, and 50 volts (respectively) are needed in order to give a current flow of 50 microamps and produce full scale deflection (f.s.d.) of the meter. We are overlooking the resistance of the meter in these calculations, and in practice the series resistances would be adjusted downwards slightly in order to give total resistances through the circuit equal to the figures given above.

If you look at each resistance and the full scale voltage it provides, you should notice that the full scale sensitivity in volts is always equal to 1 volt per 20k of series resistance. In analogue multimeter specifications you will find that instruments are often referred to as something like a "20k/volt" or "1k/volt" type. This is, in fact, usually given as the first figure in a specification sheet, and it is the most important one. The higher this figure, the more reliable d.c. voltage readings taken with the instrument will be. This is not to say that the accuracy of a 20k/volt multimeter will be better than that of a 1k/volt type (although this will often be the case). The point to note here is that an instrument with poor sensitivity can provide totally accurate but completely misleading results!

The reason this can happen is that the resistance through the multimeter is added into the circuit under investigation, and can affect the voltages in the circuit. Often this loading of the test voltages will be too small to be of any significance, but under some circumstances it can reduce test voltages by massive amounts. The circuit of Figure 2 is for a simple audio amplifier stage based on an operational amplifier, and it is the type of thing that can be found in many electronic projects for the home constructor. It is designed to give a high input impedance of around 1 megohm, and accordingly, the value of bias resistors R1 and R2 has been made quite high. The voltage at the junction of these two components is half the supply voltage, as these two resistors are of equal value. The supply potential is 10 volts, giving what is obviously 5 volts at the junction of R1 and R2. But what voltage reading would be obtained if a 20k/volt multimeter was used to measure this voltage?

This is to some extent a "how long is a piece of string" style question, and it depends on the voltage range used to make the measurement. With a supply potential of 10 volts, the 10 volt range of the multimeter would seem to be a

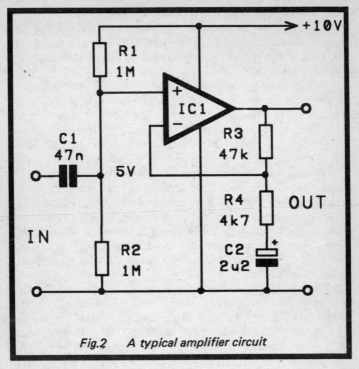

Fig.2   A typical amplifier circuit

reasonable choice. This gives a resistance of 200k through the
multimeter, and the effective circuit of Figure 3 when the
measurement is made. The 200k resistance of the meter
circuit is in parallel with R2, and a simple parallel resistance
calculation will show that it effectively reduces R2 to 166.66k
((200k × 1000k)/(200k + 1000k) = 166.66k). In terms of
voltage reading, this gives what is only about one-seventh of
the supply voltage at the junction of R1 and R2 instead of
half the supply voltage, or just over 1.4 volts rather than 5
volts. This voltage reading is a true reflection of the voltage
present in the circuit, but that voltage is only present while
the multimeter is connected into circuit, and it is not really
a valid reading.

The degree of loading is dependent on the voltage range
selected, and on the sensitivity of the meter used. The higher

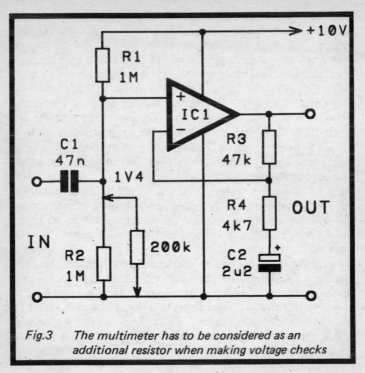

*Fig.3   The multimeter has to be considered as an
additional resistor when making voltage checks*

the sensitivity of the meter in k/volt, the less severe the
loading. There have been a few analogue multimeters which
offer 50k/volt sensitivity, and with one of these the resistance
on the 10 volt range would obviously be 500k. This would
produce far less loading if used to make our demonstration
voltage reading, but it would still effectively shunt R2 down
to a value of 333.33k, giving a voltage reading of just 2.5 volts
instead of 5 volts. Some inexpensive multimeters have
sensitivities of just 1k/volt, and with one of these set to the
10 volt range it has a resistance of a mere 10k. In the above
test this would give a reading of only around 0.1 volts, and the
deflection of the meter's pointer would probably be barely
discernable!

Using a higher voltage range provides a higher resistance
through the multimeter, and consequently gives reduced

loading. For example, using a 20k/volt instrument switched to the 100 volt range to make our example measurement, the resistance through the unit would be 2 megohms. Although this would still significantly shunt R2 and reduce the voltage reading, the actual reading would be 4 volts, which is at least getting close to the correct level of 5 volts. This method is of limited practical value though, as readings produce very little deflection of the meter's pointer. The practical result of this is readings that are difficult to take, and which will lack accuracy however painstaking you are in obtaining them. A pertinent point to remember here is that the accuracy of an analogue multimeter is normally expressed as a percentage of its full scale value. Thus, if the accuracy is 2% at full scale (which would be quite typical) then it is only guaranteed to be 20% at one-tenth of the full scale value, although in practice it would almost invariably be substantially better than this.

I would not wish to give the impression from all this that analogue multimeters always provide misleading d.c. voltage readings, and are consequently of no practical value. This is certainly not the case, and I regularly use a 20k/volt analogue instrument when testing and developing circuits. Like any test instrument, they need to be used thoughtfully if they are to be of real help. If we return to our example test circuit, looking at the high values of the bias resistors it should be obvious that severe loading of the test point will occur, and the low reading would therefore be just what was expected. The problem with a test of this type is that it is rather inconclusive, and the low reading could be due to the expected loading, or it could be that one of the bias resistors had become faulty and that the voltage was genuinely incorrect. In some cases there may be no easy way of checking this type of thing, and it might be necessary to remove and check the resistors.

Often there will be some other voltage check that can be used to give a good indication of whether or not there is a fault in that part of the circuit. In this example the obvious voltage check to make is at the output of the amplifier. Most amplifiers have unity voltage gain at d.c. to make accurate biasing easy and reliable. The voltage at the output of the amplifier should therefore be approximately 5 volts, and if it is, then it is highly unlikely that there is a fault in the amplifier or bias circuit. Remember that the output of the amplifier is at a low impedance and can provide plenty of current. The resistance of even a 1k/volt instrument on the 10 volt range is unlikely to produce noticeable loading of this voltage.

When using an analogue multimeter it is very much a matter of looking at the circuitry around the test point, and determining if any significant loading of the reading is likely to result. If it is, then any reading obtained needs to be regarded with a certain amount of caution. The exception to this is when the voltage reading is much higher than it should be. This is certainly indicative of a fault, as loading effects can only reduce voltage readings, not increase them. It is worth mentioning that some service sheets for commercial equipment provide test voltages obtained using a 20k/volt multimeter. This is very convenient provided you are using a standard 20k/volt instrument, but the different degree of loading must be taken into account if you use a different type.

As a sensitive meter will still produce loading of test voltages at times, there may seem to be no advantage in using one of these. This is not true though, and the advantage of a high sensitivity instrument is that most of the time it will not give any real problems of this type, and unambiguous results will be obtained. A 1k/volt meter will often give problems with loading, and results that lack legitimacy. The whole point of using a multimeter is to obtain conclusive information, but low sensitivity meters will often fail to provide conclusive results. A 1k/volt meter is much better than nothing, but it is a good idea to pay the extra for a 20k/volt type if you can.

A.C. Voltage
The a.c. voltage ranges use what is effectively a d.c. voltmeter circuit with a simple rectifier stage added ahead of it. The k/volt sensitivity is often lower on a.c. ranges than on the d.c. ones. Usually it is something under half the d.c. sensitivity, and I have encountered 20k/volt multimeters which offer a sensitivity of only 2k/volt on the a.c. voltage ranges. There is no obvious reason why the sensitivity should need to be

reduced for a.c. measurements, and I would presume that this is done in order to give a higher current through the rectifier circuit so that it provides better linearity. Even with reduced sensitivity, the linearity of the rectifier is not usually very good. Rather than using some electronic means of giving improved performance in this respect, the normal solution is to have separate a.c. and d.c. voltage scales, with the a.c. one being slightly non-linear so as to match the rectifier circuit and give accurate results. Due to slight differences in the characteristics of rectifiers it is not possible to produce a universal scale that will ideally suit every instrument. Therefore, the accuracy on a.c. voltage ranges is usually slightly inferior to that on the d.c. voltage ranges.

The lower sensitivity on the a.c. voltage ranges is not usually of any great consequence, since these ranges are mostly used for measuring such things as the mains supply, the output voltage from a mains transformer, and the output voltage from an audio power amplifier. All these sources are low impedance types which can supply the extra current without sagging under the strain. For audio measurements the frequency response on the a.c. voltage ranges is something that needs to be taken into account. Some of the analogue instruments that I have owned seemed to have frequency responses that extended well beyond the upper limit of the audio range and into the radio frequency spectrum. Others barely seemed to accommodate the full 20kHz audio bandwidth. I nave not yet encountered one that can not be used over the full audio range, but that is not to say that such a beast does not actually exist. If you intend to use a multimeter for this type of testing it would be as well to carefully check this aspect of its specification before deciding whether or not to buy it. Few analogue multimeters will prove to be much use for a.c. voltage checks at frequencies of more than about 100kHz.

Decibels

Most analogue multimeters have decibels (dB) ranges, or to be more precise, they have decibel scales. These operate using the a.c. voltage ranges, and permit power measurement. The main use of these scales is when making tests on audio circuits, and they are mostly used for relative rather than absolute measurements. For instance, if you are measuring the gain of an amplifier, it is just a matter of measuring the input and output levels using the decibel scales. With input and output levels of (say) +10 and +22 decibels, the gain of the amplifier is 12 decibels. Note that it does not matter what input level is used for this type of testing, provided it is within the measuring range of the unit, and it gives an output level that is within the range of the unit. In our previous example, if the input level was reduced to +6 decibels, the output level should reduce to +18 decibels, still giving a gain of 12 decibels. This is much quicker and more convenient than measuring the input and output levels in volts, and then calculating the gain from these. Its only drawback is that you have to understand the decibels system, which uses logarithmic and not linear scaling. This is why it is possible to use any desired input level that gets on-scale readings, and always get the same difference between the two readings.

The basis of the system is that an increase in voltage by a factor of ten is equivalent to an increase of 20 decibels. A further increase by a factor of ten gives a further increase by 20 decibels, as does each further tenfold boost. This system works equally well with attenuation, and a voltage reduction by a factor of ten is a drop of 20 decibels.

There are two advantages to this system. One of these is that it compresses large changes of voltage into quite modest numbers at one end of the scale, but it still permits small changes to be accurately measured at the other end of the scale. A voltage gain of 80 decibels is a gain of 10000 when expressed as a simple ratio of input voltage to output voltage. A gain of 6 decibels is a voltage gain of fractionally over 2 times when expressed as a ratio. This system keeps the numbers manageable, but it will accommodate measurements on high gain amplifiers just as well as tests for mild variations in the frequency responses of hi-fi amplifiers.

The other advantage is that it is much easier to calculate the gains or losses through a series of circuits. If a circuit has three stages which provide gains of +66, −10, and +20 decibels, the total gain is obtained simply by adding these figures together (which obviously gives an answer of 76 decibels with this example). This avoids the long multiplication and division involved when using gain figures in the form of input to output voltage ratios.

This table shows how a range of voltage ratios and decibel values compare, and should prove useful to those who are not already familiar with the decibel system of gain measurement. However, in order to take proper advantage of this system it is very much a matter of learning to think and work in decibels, without constantly converting from decibels to voltage ratios. It would probably be easier just to work in voltage ratios than to keep making conversions.

Voltage Ratio	Decibels	Voltage Ratio	Decibels
1.0	0	5.0	13.98
1.1	0.83	5.5	14.81
1.2	1.58	6.0	15.56
1.3	2.28	6.5	16.26
1.4	2.92	7.0	16.90
1.5	3.52	7.5	17.50
2.0	6.02	8.0	18.06
2.5	7.96	8.5	18.58
3.0	9.54	9.0	19.08
3.5	10.88	9.5	19.55
4.0	12.04	10.0	20.00
4.5	13.06		

Higher gains can be converted with the aid of this table. As an example, 66dB is a voltage ratio of (approximately) 2000. This is derived by first dividing 66 by 20 to find how many 20dBs (gains of ten times) it contains, which is clearly three in this case. Ten to the power of three is 1000 (10 x 10 x 10 = 1000). The 6dB that is left over is equal to a voltage ratio of almost exactly two times, and 1000 multiplied by two gives the final answer of 2000. Working the other way, and voltage ratio of (say) 800 is broken down into gains of 100 (two sets of 20dB, or 40dB in other words), and 8 (which is 18.06dB). Adding these together gives the final answer of 58.06dB.

Strictly speaking decibels are a measurement of power gain, and not voltage gain. As power (in watts) is equal to the voltage (in volts) multiplied by the current flow (in amps), a voltage ratio has to be squared in order to give the power gain. A gain of 20dB is therefore a voltage gain of 10, but a power gain of 100. This assumes that the source and load impedances are the same. Although using decibel measurement for voltage gain might not be considered strictly legitimate by everyone, in practice it is a very convenient way of doing things, and it tends to be used in this manner more than it is for true power gain measurement.

D.C. Current

Measurement of d.c. current is a standard feature, and it is achieved using a setup along the lines of Figure 4. Here a

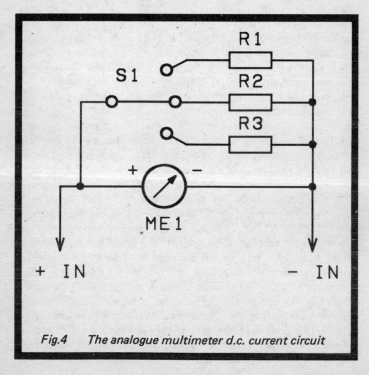

Fig.4   The analogue multimeter d.c. current circuit

11

series of low value resistors are used to shunt the meter and reduce its sensitivity. If an analogue multimeter has a high current range (about 1 amp or more) the shunt resistance will often be a piece of very stout wire, or what in some cases is a strip of steel! This is because the percentage of the current that must be channelled through the meter movement is so small that the shunt resistor requires a value which is a matter of milliohms rather than ohms. Another factor here is that thin wires would simply burn out with a strong current flow, and would be unusable anyway.

It is a little realised fact that good sensitivity is just as important for d.c. current measurement as it is for d.c. voltage tests. There are two reasons for this. The main one is simply that with an insensitive meter it is not possible to accurately measure small currents. Accurately measuring (say) a base current of around 10 microamps flowing into a transistor is quite feasible with the 50 microamp meter of a 20k/volt instrument, and on the 50 microamp range a deflection equal to about 20% of the full scale deflection will be obtained. This should give excellent accuracy. With the 1 milliamp meter movement of a 1k/volt instrument a current of 10 microamps represents only 1% of the minimum possible full scale value, and it could not be measured properly.

Whereas a voltmeter should offer the highest possible resistance, a current meter should have the lowest possible resistance. Ideally it should have zero resistance so that it only measures the flow of current, and does not hinder it in any way. In practice there must always be a certain amount of resistance through the circuit, and the exact figure will vary from one current range to another. It could be as high as two or three kilohms on the most sensitive range, which is the resistance through the meter. On higher current ranges it could be only a fraction of an ohm, and most of the resistance through the instrument would then probably be that introduced by the test prods and leads.

Unlike voltage measuring circuits, a highly sensitive meter does not necessarily give better results than a lower sensitivity type. This is due to the fact that less sensitive meter movements tend to have lower resistances than the higher sensitivity types. A 50 microamp meter with a shunt to reduce its full scale sensitivity to 1 milliamp could therefore still have a higher resistance than a 1 milliamp meter movement. What is needed for optimum results is a meter that has a combination of high sensitivity and low resistance. In practice it normally seems to be the case that higher sensitivity meters provide better results in this application than lower sensitivity types.

A point worth noting is that it is not only the reduced current caused by the series resistance of a multimeter that can produce problems. There will be a voltage drop through the multimeter and test prods, and this will give reduced voltage to the circuit under test. With temperamental circuits this could cause problems, but usually the effect of adding a current meter into a circuit is insignificant.

Very few analogue multimeters seem to offer any a.c. current measuring ranges. I suppose that this could be a useful feature, but despite having a multimeter with several a.c. current ranges for ten years or more, I have never used this facility in earnest. In fact I have not tried it out at all! The absence of a.c. current ranges on a multimeter should be considered as only a very minor minus point.

Analogue Resistance

Resistance measurement is not a strong point of many analogue multimeters. The standard method of resistance measurement is a circuit of the type shown in Figure 5. Variable resistor VR1 is adjusted so that there is precisely full scale deflection of the meter with the two test prods shorted together. With a resistance placed between the two test prods the current flow is restricted, and less than full scale deflection of the meter is produced. The higher the resistance, the lower the reading on the meter. The first point to note here is that this gives a reverse reading scale, and the resistance scales are always quite separate to the voltage and current ones.

The second point to note is that the scale is non-linear. For instance, if 100k gives a deflection to the mid-scale point, 200k would give a 25% deflection of the meter, 400k would give a 12.5% deflection, and so on. In other words, the scale is well spread out at the low value end, but it becomes increasingly cramped at higher values. This can

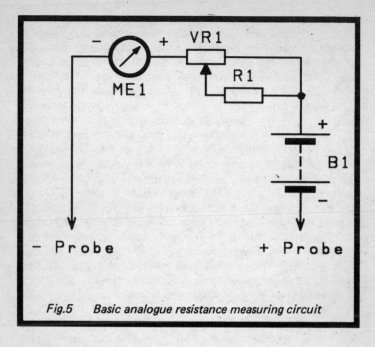

Fig.5   Basic analogue resistance measuring circuit

be a little confusing at first, but it is something that you soon get used to. It can provide very accurate results if a reasonable number of resistance ranges are included, so that resistances can always be measured at the expansive low value end of a resistance range. In practice many instruments take advantage of the fact that each range covers a very wide range of values, and only include two or three resistance ranges. This limits the accuracy at some resistances, but still gives results that are sufficient to satisfy most requirements.

Other Features
Some multimeters come complete with one or two "extras", and probably the most common of these is some form of built-in transistor tester. In most cases this is just the standard resistance measuring circuit plus a different set of test leads which include a minimal amount of extra circuitry (usually just a single resistor). It does not provide very sophisticated

14

testing, but it is perfectly adequate to sort out the "duds" from the serviceable components. This is certainly a worthwhile feature, but as we shall see later, it is one that can easily be added to practically any analogue multimeter which does not have it as a standard feature.

I have come across one or two analogue multimeters which have capacitance ranges. This is potentially extremely useful, but these ranges required external a.c. reference voltages in order to function. In practice it is unlikely that suitable reference voltages would be available, and it would probably not be worthwhile taking the trouble to install suitable (and safe) voltage sources in the workshop.

When making tests using a multimeter you should always check that it is set to the correct range before connecting it to the test circuit, not after connecting it up. In reality most of us occasionally forget to check that the instrument is on the right range, and a severe overload results. Virtually all multimeters have some form of built-in overload protection circuit, and this is usually of the electronic variety.

This almost invariably means a circuit of the type shown in Figure 6 where the series resistor and diodes form a simple clipping circuit. This ensures that the voltage across the meter can not exceed more than about 0.5 volts or so, and the meter is designed to be able to withstand this level of overload for a considerable period without sustaining damage. This type of circuit is reasonably effective, but it can not be relied upon to always fully protect the meter. For the protection circuit to be really effective the series resistor needs to be very high in value. A high voltage then forces only a small current through the circuit so that there is no damage to the resistor, the diodes, or the meter. For voltage measurements there will probably be no problem in including a high value protection resistor, but it would severely reduce performance in the current measuring mode of operation. Multimeters with electronic overload protection are often more vulnerable on the current and (possibly) the resistance ranges than on the voltage ranges.

A while ago the service engineer at one well known electronic component and equipment retailer told me that they were receiving a lot of returned multimeters which had

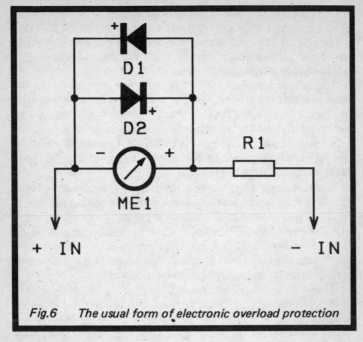

Fig.6   The usual form of electronic overload protection

sustained overload damage. The cause seemed to be that the specification stated that these multimeters could withstand 250 volts a.c., but when people tried connecting them across the 240 volt a.c. mains supply switched to various ranges, the units almost instantly sustained severe damage. Unfortunately, many of the people who had purchased these instruments had not read the specification properly, and the 250 volt a.c. overload was only applicable to the a.c. and d.c. voltage ranges and not the resistance and current ones! This is typical of multimeters which have simple electronic overload protection, and not a shortcoming which only afflicts these particular instruments.

The moral of the story is to never deliberately overload any multimeter, as they are delicate instruments which need to be treated with respect. Always be especially careful when making tests on high voltage circuits. From bitter experience, I have learned to always leave multimeters switched to a medium or high voltage range, not a resistance or current

16

range. If you get into the habit of doing this, and when you use the meter at the beginning of a session you should happen to connect it to a high voltage circuit before setting it to the right range, the chances of it becoming damaged are remote. It is definitely not a good idea to leave a multimeter switched to a current range, especially a high current range. Apart from the danger of damaging the meter itself, there is a risk that the virtual short circuit it provides on these ranges could damage the circuit under examination.

Electronic overload protection circuits are sometimes backed-up by a fuse. This can reduce the risk of prolonged overloads damaging the unit, but the fuse might act too slowly to be of much use in the event of a gross overload. Some up-market instruments have a high speed electro-magnetic cutout, and in my (less than extensive) experience of these, they certainly seem to be very effective.

One or two multimeters have featured such gadgets as signal injectors and intermediate frequency (i.f.) alignment oscillators. While this type of thing increases the scope of the instrument, the additional circuits are not really part of the multimeter circuit, but separate circuits which share the same case and power source as the multimeter.

One of the most common features of analogue multimeters is a "mirror" scale. This is merely the inclusion on the scale of an arc of mirror-finish material. Its purpose is to give improved accuracy by reducing parallax error. The needle of the meter should be quite close to the scale plate, but to avoid problems with the meter sticking it is essential to have a slight gap here. The result of this is that the reading obtained varies slightly depending on your viewing angle. The idea of the mirrored part of the scale is that when taking readings you should always move to a position where the reflection of the pointer is obscured by the pointer itself. This ensures that readings are always taken when you are directly above the pointer, so that accurate and consistent results are obtained. This is useful when optimum accuracy is essential, but for most tests it is unnecessary.

Digital Multimeters
It would probably not be too difficult to design a digital

equivalent to an ordinary moving coil panel meter, and to then use this in a conventional analogue multimeter circuit. However, this would be doing things the hard way. Also, it would give all the disadvantages of digital circuits while not really exploiting their potential advantages.

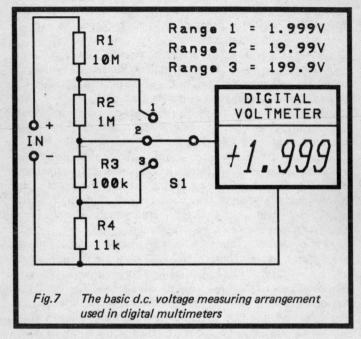

*Fig.7   The basic d.c. voltage measuring arrangement
used in digital multimeters*

For d.c. voltage measurement an arrangement of the type shown in Figure 7 is normally used. The basic digital volt-meter section of the unit would typically have a voltage range of 0 to 1.999 volts or 0 to 0.1999 volts. It would also be based on MOS integrated circuits that provide an extremely high input resistance (possibly more than one million meg-ohms). On the lowest voltage range the input signal is applied direct to the input of the meter circuit, and the chain of resistors merely serve to bias the non-earthy input to the earth rail so that a reading of zero volts is obtained with no input connected. Due to the very high input resistance this

18

biasing is essential. Without it the input could float to any voltage.

The series of resistors form a conventional step type attenuator, and the convention is to have the full scale voltage boosted by a factor of ten from one range to the next. This provides typical voltage ranges of 0 to 1.999, 19.99, 199.9, and 1999 volts. Due to the limitations of the switches and other components in the circuit, the highest voltage range is often only guaranteed to operate at voltages up to about 500 or 600 volts. Voltages above the maximum given in the specification are displayable, but could damage the unit.

With an analogue multimeter the input resistance of the instrument varies according to which range is selected, as was explained previously. The same is not true of digital units, where the input resistance is always equal to the total resistance through the attenuator, regardless of which range is in use. The input resistance of the basic voltmeter circuit is too high to have any significant effect on the overall input resistance. Due to this very high input resistance of the basic voltmeter circuit, the resistances in the attenuator can be quite high without any risk of the voltmeter circuit impairing the accuracy of the unit due to loading on the attenuator. The input resistance of digital multimeters is generally either 10 or 11 megohms. In this respect they are actually much more like the electronic analogue voltmeters (or "high impedance" voltmeters) that were very popular a few years ago, than an ordinary analogue multimeter.

You are unlikely to find any reference to so many k/volt in digital multimeter specification sheets, since this system does not really work well with this type of instrument. The sensitivity in k/volt is different for each range, because the input resistance is constant, but the full scale sensitivity is not. If the k/volt sensitivity is worked out for each range, it should give some impressive results on the low voltage ranges, but on the higher ranges results are only comparable to an analogue multimeter. As a couple of examples, with an input resistance of 10 megohms, on a 0.1999 volt range the k/volt sensitivity would be over 50000k/volt (or 50 megohms per volt in other words). On the 199.9 volt range the sensitivity would still be quite good at 50k/volt.

19

Digital multimeters have a reputation for giving totally accurate d.c. voltage readings with no loading problems, but this is something of an over-simplification. It is true that for what is probably about 99% of voltage tests there is no significant loading of the test point, but with very high impedance circuits loading of more than a few percent can still occur. For example, applying a digital multimeter having a 10 megohm input resistance to our test circuit gives the result shown in Figure 8. R2 is effectively loaded down to a

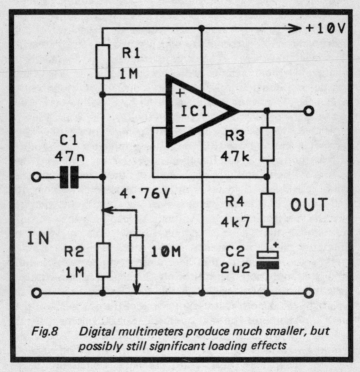

Fig.8   Digital multimeters produce much smaller, but possibly still significant loading effects

resistance of about 909k, and the voltage at the junction of R1 and R2 is reduced to about 4.76 volts. This is a reduction of only about 5%, but with very high input impedance circuits the values of R1 and R2 could be even higher. In fact values as high as 10 megohms are not unknown in this type of circuit, and this would give much more significant loading. To be precise, with 10 megohm bias resistors the voltage reading would be 3.333 volts.

Loading with a digital multimeter is clearly far less of a problem than with even one of the more sensitive analogue instruments, but the effect of the multimeter on the test circuit is still something that needs to be kept in mind.

An important advantage of digital multimeters is that for voltage and current measurements they will almost invariably accept input signals of either polarity. If the voltage or current is negative, a " − " sign to the left of the numeric digits switches on to show that a signal of reverse polarity is being measured. This is especially useful when testing equipment that has dual balanced supply rails, as test voltages can then have either polarity with respect to the central 0 volt earth rail. A dual polarity instrument can avoid a lot of swopping over of the test leads in order to obtain a signal of the right polarity.

Digital multimeters also have extra display segments which indicate an overload condition. This is important as, unlike a moving coil meter, the main display gives no clue that an overload has occurred. The overload indication should be something that is not easily overlooked, and some instruments flash the whole display on and off while an overload is present.

A.C. Voltage

The early digital multimeters were often less than impressive on their a.c. voltage ranges. This was not due to any lack of accuracy or restrictions on the voltage range covered. In fact the voltage ranges usually accommodated voltages at least as high as most analogue instruments, and at the other end of the scale a resolution of 1 millivolt or even 100 microvolts was generally achieved. The problem was a lack of frequency response. I still use a digital multimeter that I obtained what must be well over ten years ago, and it has what is in most respects a high specification. However, on the a.c. voltage ranges the frequency response rolls off very rapidly above about 200 Hertz. This is fine for measuring signals at the 50 Hertz mains frequency, but renders it virtually useless for audio testing. This is rather a pity, as its good sensitivity would permit low level audio measurements that would be impossible with ordinary analogue multimeters. Analogue instruments mostly have lowest a.c. voltage ranges of about 2.5 to 10 volts f.s.d., which only permits voltages of a few hundred millivolts or more to be measured accurately.

Looking at the specifications of modern digital multimeters shows some improvement, but the majority still seem to have an upper limit of about 400 to 1000 Hertz on their a.c. voltage ranges, which still renders them of limited use for audio frequency testing. Another point to bear in mind is that there is no digital multimeter equivalent to the decibel scales fitted to analogue types. You have to take measurements in volts and then get out the calculator!

Current
Current measurement is another area where some digital multimeters leave a lot to be desired. The usual setup for current measurement is the one shown in Figure 9. The test current flows through the resistor, and it develops a proportional voltage across the resistor. With a 100 ohm resistor for example, each milliamp of current will produce 0.1 volts across the resistor. With a voltmeter having a full scale value of 1.999 volts, this gives a direct readout in milliamps of 0 to 19.99 milliamps (with a little adjustment of the decimal point).

This gives good accurate results, and a wide range of currents can easily be accommodated by using several switched series resistors. The drawback is that some instruments (as in our above example) drop nearly 2 volts with readings at something approaching the full scale value. This can seriously reduce the test current, especially if the voltage drop causes a malfunction in the equipment being tested. I suppose that in an extreme example the supply voltage of the equipment being checked could actually be less than the maximum voltage drop through the multimeter. Errors would then almost certainly be obtained. Not all digital multimeters produce such a large voltage drop, and the higher quality types usually have a basic 0 to 0.1999 voltmeter circuit, giving a voltage drop that is always less than 200 millivolts. Some practical tests on analogue multimeters would suggest that this is very much in

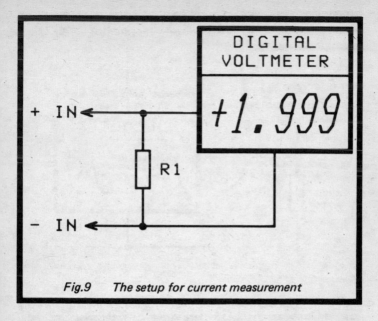

Fig.9   The setup for current measurement

keeping with the performance obtained with analogue instruments.

One advantage of digital multimeters over the analogue variety is that they are much more likely to be equipped with a.c. current ranges, although the chances are that you will never actually need to use them!

Linear Resistance

Digital multimeters are generally much better than analogue types for resistance measurements. The system used for resistance measurements is totally different to that utilized for analogue multimeters, and the basic arrangement of Figure 10 is used. The constant current source drives the test resistance, and the voltmeter measures the potential developed across this resistance. Applying Ohm's Law will show that the voltage produced across the test resistance is proportional to its value.

In practice the test current is made an amount that gives a reading directly in ohms, kilohms, or megohms. For instance,

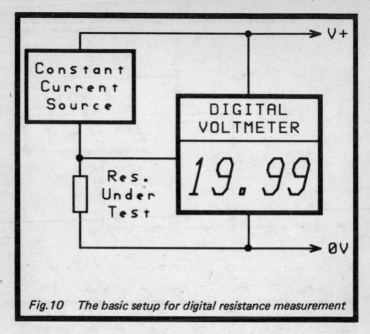

Fig.10   The basic setup for digital resistance measurement

if the test current is 1 milliamp, the output voltage is equal to 1 volt per kilohm of resistance. Assuming that the voltmeter reads from 0 to 1.999 volts, this would give a resistance readout of 0 to 1.999 kilohms. Decreasing the test current to 100 microamps (0.1 milliamps) gives 1 volt per 10 kilohms of resistance, or a range of 0 to 19.99 kilohms. Activating a different decimal point segment on the display is all that is needed in order to give a direct 0 to 19.99k readout. In this way a wide range of resistances can be accommodated, and most digital multimeters can measure resistances from 1 ohm to 10 megohms or more. Their direct digital readout in ohms, kilohms, or megohms is much more convenient than the reverse reading logarithmic scaling of analogue multimeters.

For this system to work it is essential that the voltmeter has an extremely high input resistance, so that it does not tap off a significant amount of the test current. This is particularly important on the higher resistance ranges where the test current might only be in the region of 1 microamp.

However, as pointed out previously, digital voltmeter circuits are usually based on MOS integrated circuits that provide the necessary ultra-high input impedance without the need to resort to any low input current buffer amplifiers.

Semi Digits

When looking at digital multimeter specifications you will almost certainly encounter the intriguing term "half digit" in the general descriptions of these instruments, or in the display specification. A half digit is a display digit which can only be zero or one, rather than the full 0 to 9 range. It is the most significant (i.e. the left hand) digit that is the half digit, and a three and a half digit display would therefore read from 0 to 1999.

The point of having half digits is that they give better results on low readings which just about produce an overload on one range, making it necessary to switch up a range. For instance, with a straightforward three digit display, measuring 1.042 volts on the 0.999 volt range would give an overload, and switching to the 9.99 volt range would give reduced resolution and accuracy with a reading of 1.04 volts. Most digital instruments have an accuracy which can be no better than plus or minus one digit, and the reading might therefore be 1.03 or 1.05 volts. With a three and a half digit display the 1.042 volt reading would be accommodated by the 1.999 volt range, but the added cost and complexity of the extra half digit is negligible.

Most multimeters offer three and a half or four and a half digit displays. For most purposes a three and a half digit type is more than adequate, and actually offers far better accuracy and resolution than most analogue multimeters. A four and a half digit type with 0.05% accuracy is a very impressive instrument, but how often do you need anything approaching that degree of accuracy? With most electronic testing, actual voltages, currents, etc. can depart by several percent from their nominal levels without being indicative of a fault. A three and a half digit multimeter with about 0.5 or 1% accuracy is therefore more than adequate for most testing. Four and a half digit types are better suited to research laboratories than to the amateur electronics enthusiast's workshop. It is also worth noting that the guaranteed accuracy of some four and a half digit multimeters does not merit the extra digit on some of their ranges.

My digital multimeter has a l.e.d. display and requires a large 9 volt battery. This is something of a dying breed though, and most of the instruments currently available have liquid crystal displays (l.c.d.s). Although l.c.d.s have often been of rather poor quality in the past, modern components of this type are generally much improved. They last longer, can be viewed over a much wider range of angles, and have much better contrast. Their main attraction for use in multimeters is that they consume very little current, which avoids the need for large batteries. Most l.c.d. digital multimeters are powered from a single PP3 size battery which does not even need to be a high power type. A further advantage of l.c.d.s is that they can be read easily under a wide range of light levels, and they do not appear to switch off with high ambient light levels. On the other hand, they can not be read easily (or at all) under dark conditions unless the display incorporates some form of backlight.

Extras

Most digital multimeters just seem to have basic voltage, current, and resistance ranges with no "frills". A feature that is to be found on some of the more up-market models is the ability to measure capacitance. Often the number of ranges is rather limited, but still sufficient to cover a wide range of values. Unlike most capacitance ranges on analogue instruments, no a.c. reference voltages are required, and the capacitance ranges are perfectly usable. This is probably the most useful extra feature to have.

Other extras include temperature measurement (via an external probe which might not be included as standard) and conductance ranges. Temperature measurement might not seem to be particularly relevant to electronic testing, but it can sometimes be useful to check the temperatures of power devices and their heatsinks.

Conductance is not something that is often encountered in practical electronics, and many readers may be unfamiliar with this form of measurement. It is a sort of inverse resistance, and is a measurement of how well something conducts rather than how much it resists a current flow. Whereas the formula for resistance is voltage divided by current, for conductance it is current divided by voltage. Conductance is measured in mhos, and the "mho" name, according to electronic legend, was derived by spelling "ohm" backwards! I suppose that this type of measurement could have practical applications, but with most electronics enthusiasts thinking very much in terms of resistance rather than conductance, it is the type of feature that is likely to go almost totally ignored in practice.

Some digital multimeters have a "diode check" facility which, on the face of it, is unnecessary, as a resistance range can be used for testing diodes. In fact a resistance range is not always suitable for checking silicon diodes, as these require a forward bias of about 0.5 volts before they will start to conduct. There is no problem if the multimeter uses a 0 to 1.999 volt voltmeter for resistance checks, and in the forward direction a reading of around 0.600 should be obtained. The exact figure will depend on the test current and the precise forward characteristic of the device concerned. With a 0 to 0.1999 volt voltmeter the test voltage is inadequate to bring the diode into conduction, and it apparently fails to conduct in either direction. To look at things more accurately, the diode is almost certainly being brought into conduction, but the voltage across it is beyond the full scale value of the voltmeter, and the meter gives an overload indication. The diode test facility is effectively a resistance range with an attenuator added ahead of the voltmeter, so that it does not register an overload until a voltage of something over about 0.7 volts or more is reached. This ensures that with the diode conducting, an in-range reading is obtained.

A few digital multimeters incorporate a transistor tester. This is generally something quite basic, with perhaps a single d.c. current gain range of 0 to 1999, but it should still be adequate for most purposes. It is certainly something that I would consider to be a very worthwhile extra.

Which Type?
Ideally you should try to obtain decent digital and analogue multimeters, but to start with you will probably only wish to

buy one type or the other. Probably most people would opt for a digital type, but I think that I would be inclined to choose a good analogue instrument. I have already pointed out some advantages of digital multimeters, and there is a further one which is worthy of mention here. Analogue multimeters tend to be very delicate, and must be treated with great respect. A large and sensitive meter movement is easily damaged by shocks (of the mechanical variety), and knocking most analogue multimeters off the workbench a few times is sufficient to render them useless. I have had my digital multimeter for what must be about 12 years or more and it is still going strong. In that time I must have had three or four analogue instruments. Tougher analogue multimeters can be obtained, but they are extremely expensive even if obtained as reconditioned second-hand models.

With so much in favour of digital multimeters, why bother with an analogue type at all? The real weakness of digital multimeters is the counting system used to take readings. A detailed description of digital voltmeter operation would be out of place here, but the usual scheme of things is to compare the input voltage with a steadily rising reference level. A clock signal is fed through to the counter/display circuit while the ramp voltage is below the input voltage, but as soon as the two voltages become equal the count is halted. The higher the input voltage, the greater the count reaches before it is brought to a halt. This gives a simple but effective digital voltmeter action, and one which works well with constant d.c. input levels. However, with varying voltages, even at low frequencies, things become unpredictable. Readings are then virtually meaningless and can even be quite misleading.

An analogue multimeter is somewhat more informative with varying voltages. For example, if feedback through the supply lines is causing low frequency instability in a circuit, an analogue multimeter will usually follow the voltage fluctuations, making it quite obvious what is wrong. If the test point has a steady d.c. level with brief low frequency pulses, an analogue multimeter will show the steady d.c. level and give a slight "kick" during each pulse. The effect of this type of signal on a digital multimeter varies from one instrument to another, but in most cases a very effective random number generator is produced!

With a high frequency pulse signal the pointer of a moving coil meter is not able to follow the variations in the signal voltage, but it usually registers the average voltage. This can be quite useful. For example, if the correct signal is a square-wave having peak-to-peak levels of 1 and 4 volts, then the average voltage will be 2.5 volts, and this should be the voltage registered on the meter. This is not a totally reliable test in that there could be a fault which is producing a genuine 2.5 volt d.c. level. However, at the very least this type of test gives a fair indication that all is well, or if the test voltage is incorrect it almost certainly indicates a fault condition. A digital multimeter when fed with this type of signal tends to be unpredictable in its response, and it depends to a large extent on the frequency of the pulse signal. At lower frequencies the result is generally a series of random values, while at high frequencies many digital multimeters seem to read zero (or something very close to zero).

Another application where digital instruments tend to be less than ideal is when adjusting a preset resistor to give a certain voltage at some point in a circuit (when adjusting the output bias level of a power amplifier for example). The problem is due to the high resolution and relatively slow up-dating of the display. Most digital multimeters only have the display up-dated about twice a second. A much higher rate is not too difficult technically, but it can often result in rapidly fluctuating readings that are virtually unreadable.

In this application the problem is mainly one of the slow up-dates of the display causing readings to lag behind the voltage at the test point. You adjust the preset for what is a roughly correct reading, only to find that on the next up-date that you have in fact over-shot by a considerable margin. Using an analogue multimeter there is no difficulty as it will track the voltage changes with no significant delay, and homing in on the right voltage is just a few seconds work. With a digital multimeter it becomes what is really a matter of trial and error. The preset is adjusted slightly, the multimeter is observed until a stable reading is obtained, and so on until the right reading is obtained. Matters are made worse by the high resolution of digital instruments, which can make it very difficult to obtain exactly the right reading anyway. Few voltages really need to be set up with such a high degree of accuracy, and the resolution of an analogue instrument should be sufficient.

As explained previously, digital multimeters mostly have rather poor frequency responses on their a.c. voltage ranges, and also lack decibel scales. This makes digital multimeters less useful for audio testing than analogue instruments, although the digital types do have higher sensitivities and input impedances.

Ideally an electronics workshop should be equipped with both digital and analogue multimeters. The analogue type are well suited to "run of the mill" testing, but the digital type are vastly superior for applications where a high degree of precision is required. If it is a matter of getting one type or the other, or which one to get first, the good all-round capability of analogue instruments would sway me in favour of one of these.

Chapter 2

COMPONENT TESTING

A browse through any of the main electronic component catalogues will reveal a vast range of components, and it would be unrealistic to expect even one of the better multi-meters to be able to check every type of component currently in use. On the other hand, a surprisingly large percentage of these components can be checked with the aid of a little ingenuity. We are really talking in terms of checks rather than comprehensive component analyzing. In most cases the tests will only show up serious faults and not a parameter that is just a few percent off specification. Fortunately, straightforward go/no go testing is normally all that is required.

Component testing falls into two main categories, one of which is testing newly purchased components to check that you have not been sold any "duds". Allied to this is the testing of components that have been in the spares box for some time and have had their identification or value markings obliterated, and checking components that have been obtained in untested "bargain" packs. The second category is where a component in a piece of equipment is suspected of being faulty, and a definitive check of its performance is required. This second type of testing is the more difficult, as it may not be possible to devise a satisfactory in-circuit check. Components then have to be carefully removed (or at least partially disconnected) from the equipment so that they can be checked properly.

Resistors

Resistors are about the easiest components to check as any multimeter should be able to measure over a large resistance range. When measuring very high values (around 1 megohm or more) you need to take care not to get your body resistance in parallel with the component being measured. The resistance from one hand to the other varies considerably from one person to another, and also depends on the area of skin in contact with the electrodes. It is generally around 2 megohms or so though, and would obviously degrade the accuracy of readings to an unacceptable level. What this means in practice is that you must hold the resistor in place in a way which means that only one hand comes into contact with the metal part of a test prod. This is not too difficult, but there is a lot to be said in favour of a good set of clip-on test prods which permit "no hands" connections to be made to components. Beware of some of the more inexpensive types which spring-off better than they clip-on!

Some of the cheaper multimeters can only measure resistance up to about 1 megohm, whereas resistors of up to 10 megohms are commonly used in electronic equipment. One way of giving high values resistors a rough (but useful) test using such an instrument is to connect two resistors in parallel in order to bring the combined resistance within the upper range of the multimeter. As an example, a 2.2 megohm resistor could be checked by connecting it in paralle with a 1.8 megohm resistor (Figure 11). This gives a combined resistance of 0.99 megohms, or 990k if you prefer ((1.8 x 2.2)/(1.8 + 2.2) = 0.99).

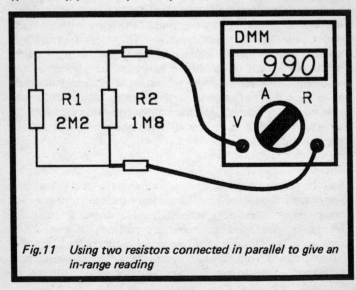

Fig.11   Using two resistors connected in parallel to give an in-range reading

Very low value resistors (below 1 ohm) can also be difficult to check, and are beyond the capabilities of some multimeters. This is one respect in which analogue multimeters seem generally to be superior to digital instruments. The latter mostly have a resolution of 1 ohm on the lowest resistance range. The well spread out scaling at the low value end of an analogue multimeter's resistance scale means that a resolution of about 0.1 or 0.2 ohms is often obtained. Even where a multimeter is equipped with a suitable resistance range, getting accurate results at low values can sometimes be difficult. A less than perfect connection anywhere in the system will produce a small but varying resistance that will make it impossible to obtain a reliable reading. I have had more than one multimeter that suffered from this problem, and which gave wavering readings on low value resistors. The problem seemed to be due to the battery being in poor contact with the battery terminals, and this application appears to be much more demanding than most others in this respect. Modern multimeters are mostly much better, and often have screw terminals which make a very firm and reliable contact with the battery.

Fortunately, very low value resistors are not often encountered in modern circuits. Unless you have a suitable multimeter, when checking these it might just be a matter of making sure that they have a very low resistance, rather than making an accurate check on their value.

In-circuit resistance measurements can be problematical, as there will often be other resistors in parallel with the one you want to measure. It is not just other resistors in the circuit that can give problems, but any component that can provide resistance is a potential cause of erroneous results. This includes inductors and transformers, but semiconductors are probably the main cause of trouble. Most resistance meters operate with a test voltage that is greater than the forward threshold voltage of a silicon junction (which is only about 0.6 volts). Any junction that is in parallel with the test resistance might shunt that resistance to give a low reading. Note that a semiconductor junction does not just mean a diode, and that two terminals of a transistor of even an integrated circuit can have the same effect.

There are various ways of combatting the parallel resistance problem, but the only one that is certain to work is to disconnect the component so that it can be isolated from the effects of other components. It is only necessary to disconnect one leadout wire in order to do this. This is an application where a digital multimeter that operates using a 0 to 0.1999 volt meter circuit is preferable to other types. The test voltage is too low to forward bias a silicon junction, and there is no risk of misleading results being obtained due to this cause. However, other parallel resistances in the circuit can still give problems, including germanium devices which have lower forward threshold voltages (although these are mostly obsolete and not often encountered these days).

When making in-circuit resistance checks there are a couple of useful points to keep in mind. One is that a semiconductor which is forward biased and giving problems can be rendered innocuous simply by reversing the test prods. What was formerly a forward biased junction then becomes a reverse biased type having an extremely high resistance. This does not guarantee that problems with parallel resistances will be avoided since there could be problems with other junctions or resistances in the circuit.

In practice this simple ploy quite often seems to be effective though. In the amplifier diode circuit of Figure 12, measuring both R2 and R3 using my analogue multimeter produced almost identical results, with a reading of about 5k. The problem is caused by the base-emitter junction of TR1 shunting R3, and the base-collector junction affecting readings when checking R2. In both cases reversing the polarity of the test prods removed the effect of the offending semiconductor junction and gave an accurate reading.

The other point to keep in mind is that parallel resistances can only produce reduced readings, and can not result in higher readings. If you measure a resistor in-circuit and the reading obtained is significantly too high, the component is certainly faulty. Of course, no power should be connected to the circuit while this type of testing is being undertaken, or the voltages developed across the test points will prevent the multimeter from functioning properly. It is possible for charged high value electrolytic capacitors to produce voltages

34

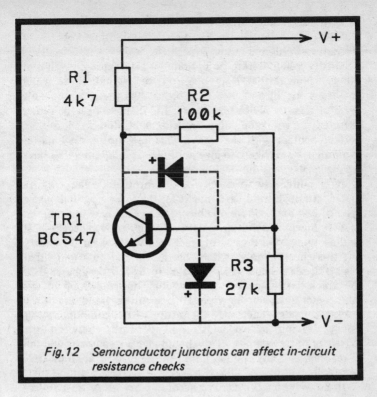

Fig.12 Semiconductor junctions can affect in-circuit resistance checks

that upset the correct functioning of the multimeter even after the power has been switched off. I have not often encountered this problem, and most electrolytic capacitors almost totally discharge soon after switch-off. The problem will usually reveal itself by producing a reading on the meter that is not steady, but instead slowly rises or falls.

Note that resistors are about the only components where in-circuit tests are likely to be at all useful. **All the other tests described in this chapter are only intended for out-of-circuit components.**

Potentiometers
Measuring the track resistance of a potentiometer is just the same as measuring the value of an ordinary resistor. Do not

be surprised if the marked values and the actual measurements differ by a substantial amount, as most potentiometers have a tolerance of plus and minus 20%.

Mostly when testing potentiometers it is not the value of the component that is in question, but whether the wiper and track are in good working order. As these components age and wear, it is not uncommon for them to become rather "scratchy", with the wiper making considerably less than perfect contact with the track. This does not always matter too much, but is likely to give poor results in circuits that have a d.c. signal across the track terminals.

It is quite easy to check for this problem using a multimeter, although mild cases might fail to show up. It is also a type of test that is more reliable using an analogue multimeter. In fact most digital multimeters will only prove successful at finding quite severe cases of track and wiper wear. To carry out this check simply switch the multimeter to a range that has a full scale value which is equal to or a little greater than the track resistance of the test component. Connect the multimeter between the wiper (the centre tag) and one of the track terminals. Then vary the setting of the component very slowly, taking it backwards and forwards between the extremes of its settings. This should give a steady rise and fall in reading, and any sudden jumps in the reading are indicative of a fault.

If the value markings have become worn away on a potentiometer, in addition to its value you will probably want to know whether it is a linear or logarithmic type. With the wiper adjusted to about the centre of its track, with a linear type there should be about equal resistance from the wiper terminal to each track connection. With a logarithmic component the two readings will differ by a substantial amount, with one reading being around five to ten times higher than the other.

With slider type potentiometers it is sometimes difficult to determine which way round they should be mounted. Linear types are symmetrical and can be mounted either way up, but logarithmic types must be mounted the right way round in order to give a good control characteristic. Few types seem to have any form of "this way up" message marked on them. Using the same test procedure as the one just described, the bottom end of the track is the one which has the lower track to wiper resistance.

Thermistors and Cds Cells

A thermistor is a form of resistor, but its resistance is temperature dependent. The resistance at room temperature varies enormously from one type to another, but this list gives the typical resistances for some popular types at 25 degrees Centigrade.

Thermistor Type	Resistance
VA1038	1k5
VA1039	470R
VA1040	150R
VA1055S	15k
VA1056S	47k
VA1066S	4k7
VA1067S	150k
GL23	1k65

These are negative temperature coefficient devices (as are virtually all thermistors), and their resistance at room temperature (which is generally about 18 to 20 degrees Centigrade) will be somewhat higher than the figures quoted above. The tolerance on thermistor ratings is quite high, and is usually 20%. Any reading of around the figures quoted above to around 40% higher would therefore be perfectly acceptable. If you hold the thermistor between two fingers while measuring its resistance, the heat from your fingers should cause the resistance to fall, probably to something slightly below the figures given above.

This is obviously a rather crude form of testing, but it will suffice for most purposes. Most components either function perfectly or do not work at all, and there are very few that are just marginally out of specification. Consequently, this type of testing will almost invariably show up any "dud" devices. However, if you have precise information on the specification of a thermistor, it would be possible to subject it to a range of known temperatures, note the resistance in each case, and then check these against the specification sheet.

A few thermistors are of the so-called "self-heating" variety. These are contained in an evacuated glass envelope, and they are heated by the current flowing through them rather than taking up the same temperature as the surrounding air. The point of the vacuum inside the glass envelope is, as far as possible, to isolate the sensing element from its surroundings. The most popular of these (and about the only readily available type) is the R53, or RA53 as it seems to be referred to in some catalogues. This is mostly used in the gain stabilisation circuits of high quality audio signal generators. It is difficult to test properly, but measuring its resistance on each range of a multimeter should produce a different result. This is due to the fact that a lower current flows on the higher resistance ranges, and this factor is common to both analogue and digital multimeters. The lower resistance ranges should therefore give greater heating of the device, and a lower reading. These are delicate components though, and it is probably best not to use the lowest resistance ranges where there could be a risk of exceeding the component's maximum permissible dissipation.

Cadmium sulphide photocells can be given a rough check using the resistance ranges of a multimeter. These have a resistance that varies according to the light level they receive. Increased light level produces decreased resistance. With most types the variation in resistance is so large that it can be detected with no difficulty. For example, the popular ORP12 device has a resistance of many megohms in total darkness, but under very bright light it exhibits a resistance that is usually under one hundred ohms.

Capacitance

If you are lucky enough to have a digital multimeter that includes capacitance ranges you should have no difficulty in testing most capacitors. Without such a multimeter, or some other capacitance measuring instrument, some basic checks are still possible. Capacitors can have values that are outside the acceptable range, but when these components become faulty they normally produce a virtual short circuit, or go

38

closed circuit. The basic construction of a capacitor is to have a very thin layer of insulation (called the "dielectric") between two electrodes. In order to obtain high values within a small casing it is normal to have two layers of insulation and very thin foil electrodes, with the four layers being rolled up to give the familiar tubular and squashed tubular shapes. This gives large areas of electrode in a small space, but the slightest flaw in the dielectric will produce a short circuit between the electrodes.

In my experience faults of this type seem to be very rare, and presumably it is something that is not likely to occur if it is avoided at the manufacturing stage. Any components which are produced with this fault will presumably be filtered out by the manufacturer's testing procedures. A broken connection between one of the leadout wires and its electrode seems to be a more common fault. Leadout wires breaking off completely is far from rare, and some types of capacitor seem to be far less tough than resistors and most other simple electronic components.

A check for short circuits can be made using the resistance ranges of a multimeter. When you initially connect the multimeter it is quite likely that a low reading will be obtained, but this should quickly rise to a very high level. This is due to a surge of current flowing as the capacitor charges up. As the capacitor charges to the source voltage provided by the multimeter, the charge reduces and eventually becomes insignificant. Just how long it takes the capacitor to fully charge depends on the resistance range used and the value of the capacitor. A high value gives a long charge time, as does a high resistance range with its low test current.

With low value capacitors of a few hundred nanofarads or less it should not matter too much which range is used, and with a serviceable component a high reading should soon be obtained. In fact there may be no noticeable charge-up period at all with very low capacitors (a few hundred picofarads or less). With higher value components it is better to use a low resistance range so that the charge time is kept reasonably short. With electrolytic capacitors this brings the problem that the test prods must be connected to the test components with the right polarity.

With digital multimeters things are very much as one would expect, with the positive test lead connecting to the " + " terminal of the capacitor, and the negative test lead connecting to its " − " terminal. This is not the case with analogue multimeters, where the opposite method of connection is required. Having the negative battery terminal connected to the positive test lead of the multimeter might seem an unlikely way of doing things, and one which would fail to work. However, if you refer back to Figure 5 in Chapter 1 (the basic analogue resistance meter circuit) you will find that this is in fact the way things are connected. If you imagine a link across the test prods, you will see that this does give a signal of the correct polarity across the meter movement.

Although most capacitors have leakage resistances of many megohms, and will probably give a final reading that is beyond the measuring capabilities of the multimeter, some capacitors have relatively low leakage resistances. These are the electrolytic types, especially the very high value types (around 47 microfarads and upwards). High value capacitors are mainly used in supply decoupling applications, and even a resistance as low as a few tens of kilohms would then normally be quite acceptable. For more demanding applications, such as a d.c. blocking capacitor in the negative feedback network of a hi-fi preamplifier, a somewhat higher resistance might be needed in order to give satisfactory results. Lower value electrolytics of around 0.47 to 10 microfarads are often used to provide interstage coupling in audio circuits, and a leakage resistance of a few megohms is then usually needed for really reliable operation. Just what constitutes an acceptable leakage level is very much dependent on the application, and high quality components must be used where the application demands it. Be careful to connect the test prods round the right way, as a low leakage resistance could be erroneously indicated if the polarity is incorrect. Note that tantalum bead capacitors are also a polarised type, and that with some of these there is a risk of damaging them if the applied signal is of the wrong polarity.

Value Gauging
When testing capacitors with a multimeter, the "jump" of the

meter when it is first connected to a capacitor can be used to roughly gauge the value of the component. High value capacitors will give quite a large deflection of the meter, and there should be little difficulty in gauging their value. Smaller types, even if checked on the highest resistance range, will give quite small deflections, and are more difficult to test with a worthwhile degree of accuracy. A useful ploy here is to connect the capacitor with one polarity, and to then quickly connect it with the opposite polarity. This will give double the deflection when it is connected the second time (provided you do not touch both leadout wires and discharge the capacitor through your body resistance during the changeover).

The only way to convert the amount of deflection into an approximate capacitance value is to test a number of fully operational capacitors having a range of values and to note the results. These can then be compared with readings taken from test components in order to arrive at a "guestimated" value. I make no claims of great accuracy being possible, but it should show up any medium to high value capacitor which has a value that is well away from the correct one. A lack of any deflection of the meter indicates that the test component has gone open circuit, but note that very low value components (about 1 nanofarad or less) will not give a noticeable deflection of the meter. Therefore, these can not be checked for an open circuit fault using only a multimeter.

Basically the same method can be used with digital multimeters, although I must admit that I find it relatively awkward with these. Also, the ploy of connecting a capacitor with one polarity and then the other could be a little risky with digital instruments (although my multimeter seems to survive the experience). Anyway, you have been warned!

Diodes and Rectifiers

Some multimeters have a built-in diode check facility, but where this is absent it is usually possible to use the resistance ranges. As explained in the previous chapter, there can be difficulties in using digital multimeters that are based on a 0 to 0.1999 volt voltmeter for diode checking, as the full scale resistance is indicated at a voltage that is well below the forward threshold voltage of a silicon junction. Multimeters of these type almost invariably have a separate diode check facility. It does not matter too much which resistance range is used for checking rectifiers and diodes, although I suppose that there is some advantage in using the highest range. With diodes that have only low maximum forward current ratings this should ensure that there is no risk of damaging the test components. Also, if a diode should have a small but significant reverse leakage level, a high resistance range will show up the inadequate reverse resistance more readily.

The basic test procedure using an analogue multimeter is shown in Figure 13. First the multimeter is connected across the diode with the positive test lead connected to the cathode, and a fairly low resistance should be indicated. Note that the exact resistance is not relevant, but with most instruments the meter's pointer will move well across the scale. Germanium devices generally produce a lower resistance reading than do silicon types (although this is due to their lower voltage drop and not what could accurately be described as lower resistance). This checks that the diode will conduct in the forward direction, and a very high or infinite indication from the meter indicates that the component has gone open circuit. Next the test prods are swopped over, and with a reverse bias there should be no significant current flow through a silicon test device. An infinite resistance reading should therefore be obtained.

The situation is a little different with germanium diodes (such as the popular OA90 and OA91 types) where significant reverse leakage currents are quite common. A reverse resistance of around 100k or more does not indicate a fault, and circuits which use germanium diodes should be designed to take into account the possibility of a relatively high leakage current. A reverse resistance of less than 100k will be acceptable in some applications, but a diode which provides a reverse resistance of much less than this figure is of dubious quality and use.

Testing diodes and rectifiers using a digital multimeter is much the same, but the polarity of the test leads must be the opposite of that shown in Figure 13. In other words, the forward conductance test requires the positive test lead to be connected to the anode of the diode, while for the reverse

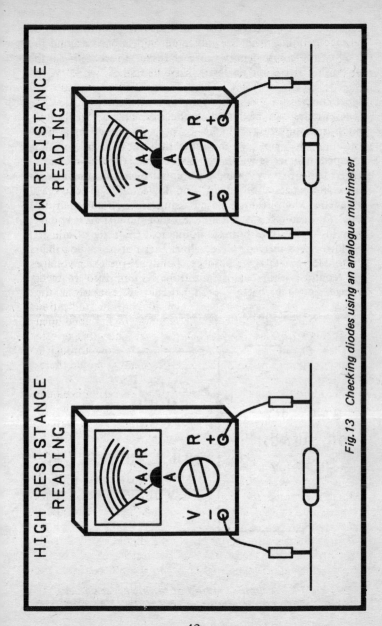

Fig.13   Checking diodes using an analogue multimeter

leakage test the positive test lead must be connected to the cathode terminal (the one indicated by the band around the body of the component). In other respects this testing is the same using digital and analogue instruments.

Zener Diodes

Zener diodes can be tested in the manner described above, but this simply shows whether or not they are giving a diode action. It does not give any indication of whether or not the avalanche voltage is within the acceptable range. Some multimeters use a battery having a potential of 9 volts or more on the highest resistance ranges, and lower voltage zeners will avalanche when reverse biased using an instrument of this type. This can give a rough indication of the operating voltage, with lower readings corresponding to higher zener voltages.

However, a proper voltage check can not be made using a multimeter alone. On the other hand, proper checking does not require a great deal of additional equipment. In fact a voltage source (a battery or a bench power supply) plus a

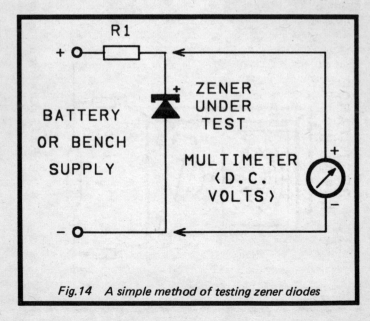

Fig.14   A simple method of testing zener diodes

resistor are the only additional components that are needed. The test setup is shown in Figure 14, and this can be put together in a matter of seconds on a solderless breadboard if the necessary materials are to hand.

The idea of the test is to feed the zener diode from a voltage source that is somewhat higher than the zener's avalanche voltage. A series resistor restricts the current flow to an acceptable level, and a multimeter set to a suitable d.c. voltage range measures the voltage across the zener diode. Zener diode voltages are normally measured at a current of 5 milliamps, and the value of R1 should be approximately 200 ohms per volt difference between the zener rating and the supply voltage. For example, with a 6.8 volt zener and a 9 volt battery as the power source, the voltage difference is 2.2 volts (9 − 6.8 = 2.2). 2.2 multiplied by 200 is 440, giving a value of 440 ohms for R1. This is not a preferred value, but the nearest preferred value above the calculated figure (which would be 470 ohms in this case) will suffice.

The same basic procedure can be used to determine the voltage of a zener diode which has had its identification markings worn away. Obviously there is no way of calculting the right value for R1 when the avalanche voltage is an unknown quantity. Start using a value of 1k for R1, which should limit the current flow to a safe level and provide a reasonably accurate avalanche voltage reading. If a highly accurate reading is required, the value of R1 can be adjusted to a more appropriate one, and a new reading then taken.

Transistors
If you are lucky enough to have a multimeter with a built-in transistor tester function you should need to do no more than follow the instruction leaflet. Without this feature ready made for you, it is not too difficult to add it to your multimeter.

Taking analogue multimeters first, all that is needed for leakage testing is a setup of the type shown in Figure 15. The multimeter is switched to its highest resistance range for this test. Note that the test leads are connected with one polarity for n.p.n. transistors, and with the opposite polarity for p.n.p. devices. Be careful not to touch the base terminal when

45

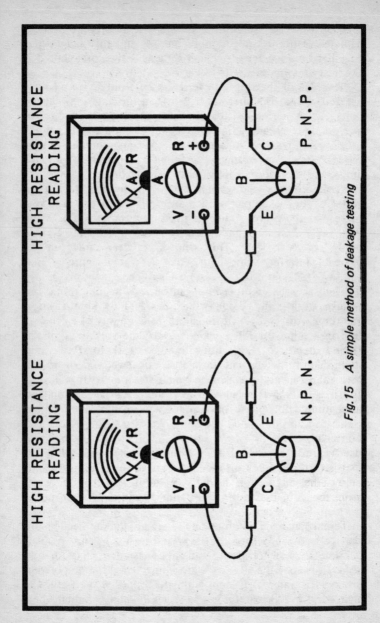

Fig.15   A simple method of leakage testing

46

making this test, as to do so would almost certainly produce erroneous results. The leakage current of a silicon transistor is generally guaranteed to be under a microamp, and is typically very much less than this. Accordingly, with a serviceable silicon transistor there should be an extremely high reading, with probably no deflection of the meter's pointer at all. A silicon device which shows significant leakage may still be operational in other respects, and might still be usable. However, in my experience, silicon transistors which have high leakage levels tend to have poor performance in other respects as well, and are not very reliable in use.

Germanium transistors are a different proposition, and there is nothing unusual in these having quite high leakage currents, particularly the higher power types. Circuits which utilize germanium transistors have to have bias circuits which compensate for the high and inconsistent leakage levels so that repeatable results are obtained. This makes it difficult to judge just what is an acceptable leakage level, and what is not. There is no hard and fast border-line for germanium transistors in general. Even if you can find specific leakage current data for the device you are testing, it could be difficult to correlate this with the resistance readings on the meter. This really has to be a subjective judgement.

Probably the best way of tackling the problem is to check a few germanium transistors that are known to be fully operational, and this will give an indication of the sorts of leakage level that are definitely acceptable. As most germanium transistors are now well and truly obsolete, and they are not normally found in current designs, you may well have no need to bother with checking this type of transistor at all.

If a test device passes the leakage test, a rough measurement of its current gain can then be made. Figure 16 shows the arrangement used when making gain measurements on n.p.n. devices, while Figure 17 shows the slightly modified arrangement used for p.n.p. types. It is essentially the same setup that is used for leakage testing, but a resistor has been added between the collector and base terminals of the test device. This provides a small base current to the transistor, which produces a much larger current flow in the collector circuit. With (say) a 10k base feed resistor, the resistance reading with

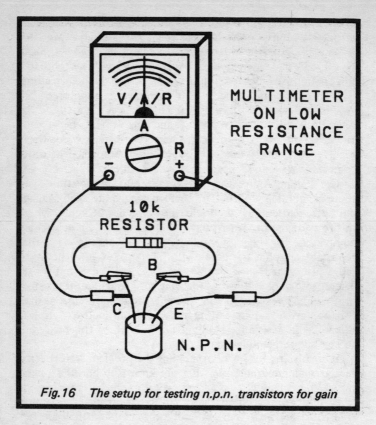

Fig. 16   The setup for testing n.p.n. transistors for gain

a functioning device should therefore be much less than 10k. The higher the gain of the transistor, the lower the resistance that will be registered on the meter. It is important to choose a resistance range that provides the test transistor with a reasonably high operating current, and one which has a mid-scale value of something in the region of 100 to 500 ohms should be suitable. The suggested value of 10k for the base feed resistor should then give good results, although a different value can be used if practical experience indicates a higher or lower value would be more suitable.

This is essentially the same setup used in some analogue multimeters which have a built-in transistor tester function.

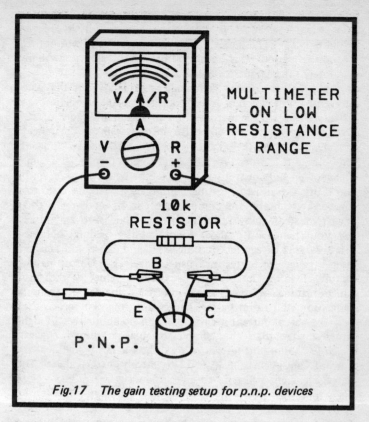

Fig.17 The gain testing setup for p.n.p. devices

In some cases the base feed resistor and n.p.n./p.n.p. switching are included in the main unit, but sometimes the resistor is included in a different set of test leads that are used for transistor testing. While it might be possible to modify a multimeter to build a transistor tester function into it, for a do-it-yourself version building up a set of test leads with the resistor added in is probably the more practical approach.

The main drawback of an improvised transistor checker of this type is that there is no gain scale ready calibrated on the meter. It would probably be possible to produce one of these using rub-on transfers, and with the aid of some test transistors of known gain to provide the calibration points. Moving coil meters are extremely delicate though, and the calibration process would need to be undertaken very carefully in order to avoid damaging the meter. With multimeters still within their guarantee period, this recalibration would almost certainly invalidate the guarantee.

An accurate current gain scale is probably not that vital anyway. The tolerances on transistor gain parameters are usually huge, with something like an acceptable range of 100 to 500 being quite typical. Also, current gains in data sheets are given at specific collector currents and voltages, but with this simple test procedure the exact figures involved are something of an unknown quantity (a factor which is common to most other transistor testing equipment). Simple transistor checkers are useful for comparative checks, and it is a good idea to test as many fully operational transistors as you can lay your hands on. Make a note of the readings obtained from various categories of transistor, and these will act as a useful gauge when testing suspect devices. Unfortunately, simply dividing the base feed resistor's value by the resistance reading on the meter will not provide an accurate indication of current gain. Things are not as simple as this, and the actual current gain is likely to be about two to eight times higher than this simple calculation would suggest.

Note that if the test device exhibits a fairly high leakage current, any gain check is of relatively little value. The leakage current will tend to give inflated gain readings. Note also, that with power devices the gain readings will often be quite low. This is partially due to the fact that most power transistors do not have very high current gains, but it is to some extent caused by power devices only working efficiently at relatively high collector currents. In transistor data tables the gains of power transistors are often quoted at collector currents of 2 amps or more! Better results might be obtained with power devices by switching to a lower resistance range, and using a lower value base feed resistor (about 1k should do). Do not test small signal transistors on a low resistance range as their maximum collector current rating might be exceeded.

The same general setup can be used with a digital multimeter, but the test prods must be connected the opposite way round. Thus, when testing an n.p.n. transistor it is the negative test prod that connects to the emitter, and the positive prod which connects to the collector. This method of transistor testing will not work with a multimeter that uses a 0 to 0.1999 volt voltmeter as the basis of the resistance measuring ranges. An over-range indication will be provided before a high enough voltage to bias the test device into conduction is achieved. The 1k range and a base feed resistance of 10k should provide good results with most digital multimeters.

Improved Tester

If you require more accurate results the simplest test circuits of Figure 18 (n.p.n.) and Figure 19 (p.n.p.) can be used. This is still a very simple test setup which can easily be breadboarded. The 9 volt battery and R1 provide a base current of approximately 10 microamps to the test device. The multimeter is switched to its 10 milliamp d.c. range, and R2 protects the meter against severe overloads if the test device should happen to have a short circuit between its collector and emitter terminals. With a digital multimeter, provided you ignore the decimal point, the reading is approximately equal to the current gain of the test device. Current gain is, of course, equal to the collector current divided by the base current. With an analogue multimeter the scale readings must be multiplied by one hundred in order to give a d.c. current gain figure, or there may be a 0 to 1000 scale that can be used for readings direct in current gain. Note that although this test setup gives a reasonably accurate gain measurement, the test is still at an indeterminate collector current and voltage. It is essential to bear this point in mind when comparing test results with current gain ranges on data sheets.

The same test circuit can be used for leakage checks, but the base terminal of the device under test should be left unconnected. This test will be more meaningful if the multimeter is switched to a lower current range so that any detectable leakage current can be measured more accurately.

VMOS

Field effect transistors are comparatively difficult to test. It is not too difficult to devise simple test circuits, but in

51

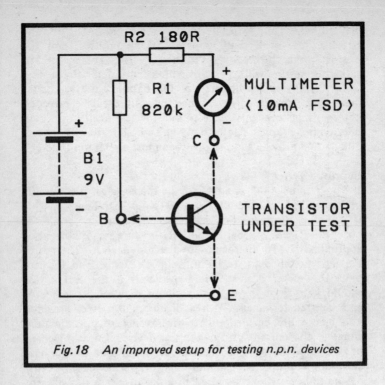

Fig.18 An improved setup for testing n.p.n. devices

practice there seems to be a real risk of damaging the test component. This is something that I have cleverly managed to achieve on several occasions! In-circuit voltage checks seem to be a better way of testing junction gate field effect devices (such as the popular 2N3819).

VMOS transistors are a different matter, and a rough check of these can be made quite easily. Although these are static sensitive components, they mostly incorporate a zener diode at the input which provides effective static protection. With these devices no anti-static handling precautions are required, but due care must be taken with any types which do not have some form of efficient built-in protection circuit.

There are strong similarities between the characteristics of VMOS transistors and ordinary bipolar types. Unlike junction

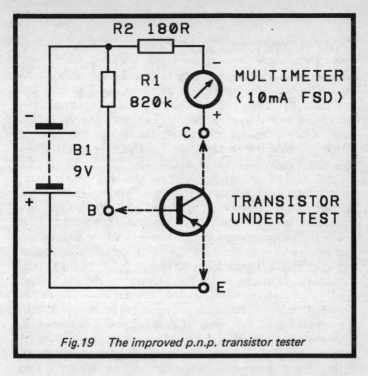

Fig.19   The improved p.n.p. transistor tester

gate field effect transistors, VMOS types are enhancement
mode and not depletion mode devices. They are normally
switched off, and are switched on by applying a forward bias.
This is very much like a bipolar transistor, and it makes them
very much easier to test. However, there are some important
differences between these two types of transistor. A bipolar
transistor is current operated, and its gain is usually expressed
in terms of the ratio of input current to output current.
VMOS transistors have extremely high input impedances
(usually at least thousands of megohms) and have negligible
input currents. Their gain is normally expressed as a form of
conductance, or in terms of input voltage and output current
in other words. The terminals of a field effect transistor have
different names to those of bipolar devices. The base, emitter,
and collector of a bipolar transistor are equivalent to the gate,

53

source, and drain terminals (respectively) of a field effect type.

One way of checking VMOS transistors is to use a multimeter set to a middle resistance range in what is virtually the same setup suggested previously for bipolar transistor checking. The base feed resistor is irrelevant though, since the gate current is insignificant. Also, the gate should be connected to the source terminal rather than just left unconnected when making leakage checks. The input resistance of VMOS transistors is so high that stray pick up might otherwise bias the test devices into conduction.

This method of testing works better with some multimeters than with others. The basic problem is that the forward bias voltage needed to bring a VMOS transistor into conduction is generally somewhat more than is needed to drive a bipolar device. Some VMOS transistors have a minimum threshold voltage of around 0.8 volts, which is not much higher than the typical figure of about 0.6 volts for bipolar transistors. However, with VMOS transistors the bias voltage needs to be taken some way beyond the threshold level before the device will conduct quite strongly, and the threshold voltage can be 2.5 volts or more. I have not found any problems when making this kind of check using my analogue multimeter (which uses 3 and 9 volt batteries for resistance testing). With some multimeters though, the bias voltage needed to bring some VMOS transistors into conduction might be greater than the available drive voltage.

More reliable results can be obtained using the simple test setup of Figure 20. The multimeter acts as a current meter to monitor the drain current of the test device, while R2 provides current limiting to protect both the multimeter and transistors under test. The multimeter should be set to a range which has a full scale value of about 10 milliamps or so. R1 limits the input current to the test device, but due to the very high input impedances of VMOS transistors this does not normally have any effect. It is only needed if the device being checked should prove to be faulty, or if it should be connected incorrectly.

This test circuit provides a forward bias of about 9 volts to the test transistor, and this should be more than ample to

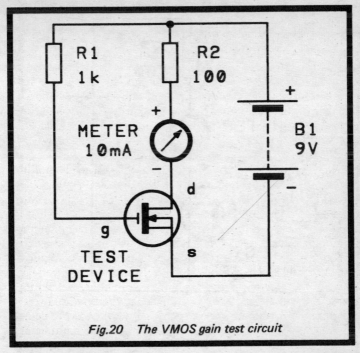

Fig.20   The VMOS gain test circuit

drive it hard into conduction. The meter should therefore read something approaching its full scale value. The exact reading will vary somewhat, depending on such factors as the precise battery voltage and the resistance through the multimeter. However, the resistance through the VMOS transistor should always be so low that there will be no significant variation from one device to another. A reading which is even slightly lower than normal would therefore suggest that the test transistor is faulty.

In order to check that the readings from this first test are due to real gain, rather than just a closed circuit test device, try changing the connection to R1, as shown in Figure 21. This gives zero bias to the transistor under test, and it should then pass only an insignificant leakage current (about 1 microamp or less).

It is possible to check P channel VMOS transistors using

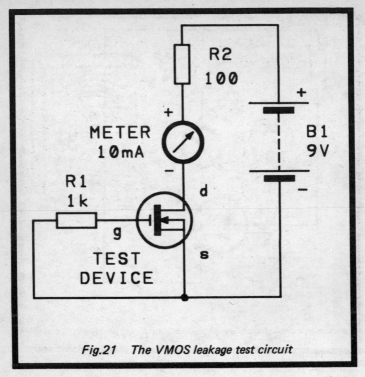

Fig.21 The VMOS leakage test circuit

essentially the same arrangement, but the polarity of the battery and the multimeter should be reversed.

Power MOSFETs

Power MOSFETs are very similar to VMOS transistors as far as their basic characteristics are concerned, but they are generally more vulnerable to damage by static charges. Destructive oscillation can also result from testing procedures, and this type of transistor needs to be tested very carefully. All the more so, as apart from being easily damaged, they are also quite expensive.

The simple method of testing suggested by Hitachi (who are the originators of these devices) is to use a multimeter set to a resistance range. Any resistance range should suffice, but it is probably best to select an intermediate one. First

56

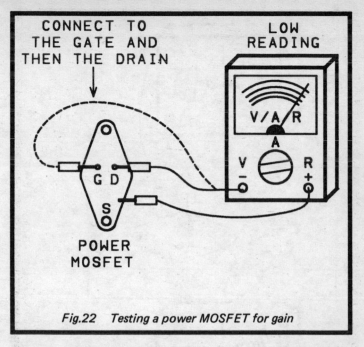

CONNECT TO
THE GATE AND
THEN THE DRAIN

LOW
READING

V/A/R

A

V
—

R
+

G D

S

POWER
MOSFET

Fig.22   Testing a power MOSFET for gain

connect the positive test lead to the source, and the negative test lead to the gate. Then move the negative test lead over to the drain (as in Figure 22). The idea of this is to first put a positive charge on the gate, and to then check that this gives a low drain to source resistance. The reading on the meter should therefore be very low. However, having charged the gate terminal, you must be careful not to touch it and alter the charge voltage. I found the easiest way of making this type of check was to fix the transistor being tested to the workbench using that indispensible servicing aid, Bostik "Blue-Tak".

The next stage of the test is to connect the negative test lead to the source terminal, and to then touch the positive test prod onto the gate leadout. This gives the gate a negative (reverse) bias, and should cut off the transistor. To check this, the positive test prod is connected to the source once again, and the negative test prod is connected

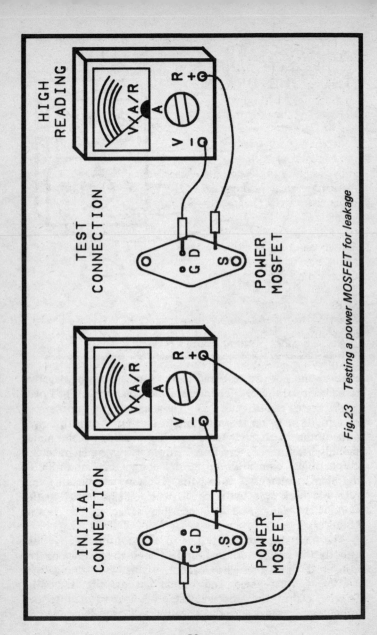

Fig.23 Testing a power MOSFET for leakage

58

to the drain terminal. A very high reading should then be obtained (see Figure 23).

As described above the test is only suitable for N channel power MOSFETs. The same procedure can be used for P channel devices though, and it is merely necessary to connect the test prods with the opposite polarity to that used for N channel types.

It should be possible to use the same test procedure with most digital multimeters. However, the procedure described above is then the correct one for P channel devices, and the test prods must be reversed for every stage of the procedure when checking N channel devices.

Incidentally, on trying this method with several VMOS transistors and three multimeters (two analogue and one digital type) it seemed to work properly in every case. It might be a worthwhile alternative to the VMOS test procedure described previously.

SCRs
The thyristor is the most simple form of SCR (silicon controlled rectifier). It does not normally conduct between its anode and cathode terminals, but it can be triggered into conduction by applying a forward bias current of around 20 milliamps to its gate terminal. It then continues to conduct until the anode to cathode current falls below about 10 milliamps.

As a very rough check of a thyristor the resistance range of a multimeter can be used to check that the suspect device does not conduct between its anode and cathode terminals with the test prods connected either way round. A rough check of the gate can be made by applying a similar test to the gate and cathode terminals. These should give a diode action (with the cathode, as one would expect, acting as the cathode terminal of the diode).

A better check can be made using a multimeter set to a low resistance range using the process outlined in Figure 24. First connect the positive test prod to the cathode, and the negative test prod to the anode (use the opposite method of connection for digital instruments of course). Briefly short circuit the gate terminal to the anode, and a fairly low reading should be obtained. When this short circuit is removed, a low reading

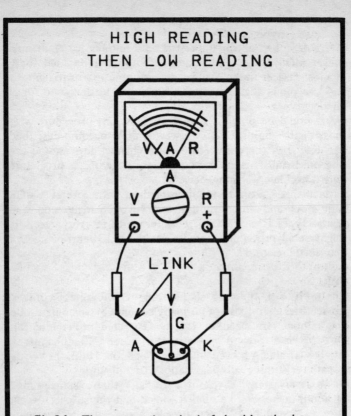

**HIGH READING
THEN LOW READING**

LINK

Fig.24   The suggested method of checking thyristors

should still be obtained as the thyristor will have been triggered, and the current flow should be sufficient to give the hold-on effect. A low resistance range must be used though, as the current flow might otherwise be insufficient to give triggering or to provide the hold-on effect. If one of the test prods is disconnected and then reconnected again, the thyristor should switch off and a high resistance reading should be obtained once more.

A triac is a bidirectional thyristor, and its MT1 and MT2 terminals are roughly equivalent to the cathode and anode (respectively) of a thyristor. The third terminal is still called the gate incidentally. Much like a thyristor, a resistance check should indicate a very high resistance between the MT1 and MT2 terminals regardless of the polarity of the test leads. A gate to MT1 resistance check is not quite the same as the thyristor equivalent in that a fairly low resistance reading should be obtained with the test prods connected either way round.

Using the trigger/hold-on test procedure for thyristors that was described previously should give exactly the same result with triacs. However, there is a difference in that it should work regardless of the polarity of the test leads. Remember, a triac is used for controlling a.c. loads. It will conduct in both directions once triggered, and it can be triggered by a gate bias current of either polarity.

Note that some triacs have a built-in diac at the gate terminals. There is no simple and really effective test procedure for these components. A resistance check should reveal a very high resistance between any two terminals, with the test prods connected either way around. Diacs themselves are similarly difficult to check. They are similar to triacs, but have no gate input. Instead, they are triggered when they are subjected to a voltage of more than a certain threshold level (typically about 30 to 35 volts). A resistance check should reveal an extremely high resistance with the test prods connected with either polarity. Beyond this, there is no simple way of properly checking a diac using a multimeter.

LEDs

Light emitting diodes (l.e.d.s) can be checked in much the same way as ordinary diodes. The obvious difference is that when the diode is conducting it should light up. This is dependent on one of the lower resistance ranges being used, since on the higher ranges there may be insufficient current to produce a significant light output level. It is probably best not to use the lowest resistance range, as with many multimeters this gives a current that is higher than the maximum rating of most l.e.d.s. A little experimentation should soon show which range gives good but not excessive brightness.

This test is a very useful one because many l.e.d.s have no

obvious polarity marking, and most methods of indicating
l.e.d. polarity are ambiguous. Often the cathode is indicated
by a shorter leadout wire or by a "flat" on the body of the
component. However, some components seem to use the
"flat" or shorter lead to denote the anode, which severely
devalues both systems. A check with a multimeter is a quick
way of incontrovertibly establishing which leadout is which.

Photo-Transistors

There is really no difference between an ordinary transistor
and a photo-sensitive type other than their types of encap-
sulation. An ordinary transistor has an opaque package
while a photo-sensitive type has a "window" (possibly
fitted with a lens) to let the light get through to the semiconductor chip. With the "window" covered to exclude
light from the chip, a photo-transistor should therefore
behave on test just like any other transistor, and can be
tested in the same way. When a photo-transistor is subjected
to fairly high light levels its leakage resistance becomes
relatively low. A multimeter switched to a middling resistance
range should clearly show this increased leakage current.

The situation is much the same with photo-diodes. They
are (more or less) standard diodes, but they have a leakage
resistance that decreases as the applied light level is increased.
The problem with photo-diodes is that they have very low
levels of sensitivity when compared to most other opto-
sensors. Even using the highest resistance range of your
multimeter it could take a very strong light in order to produce a measurable reduction in the leakage resistance. A
useless but interesting fact is that light emitting diodes will
also act as light sensitive diodes. If you measure the leakage
resistance of a large l.e.d. and then shine a bright light into
its lens, you will probably notice a small but significant
reduction in its leakage resistance.

Loudspeakers

Loudspeakers can be checked using the lowest resistance
range of a multimeter. The resistance through the component should be not very much different to its impedance rating.
The resistance usually seems to be marginally lower than the

impedance rating, but we are talking in terms of a discrepancy of just a few percent here. As the multimeter is connected and disconnected there should be a quiet "click" sound from the loudspeaker.

This is not a comprehensive test in that it only checks that there is no lack of continuity through the component, and that it produces some sound from an input signal. There could still be problems with a lack of efficiency or poor audio quality due to mechanical problems. These can only be detected by feeding an audio signal to the loudspeaker and listening to the quantity and quality of the output.

The same resistance test can be applied to headphones and earphones. A point to note is that crystal earphones work on a different principle to loudspeakers and dynamic phones. As far as the resistance test is concerned, the difference is that a very high resistance should be indicated.

Transformers and Inductors
The main faults with transformers and inductors are breaks in the windings or "shorted" turns. The first of these problems is easily diagnosed by a resistance check. The resistance through an inductor or transformer winding is usually quite low, with actual figures ranging from less than an ohm to perhaps as much as a few tens of kilohms for a specialised audio transformer. A break in a winding will normally show up as an out-of-range resistance reading.

Detecting "shorted" turns is decidedly more tricky. In theory the short circuited turns of the winding will give a reduced resistance that can be measured. In practice this reduced resistance may be too small to be detectable using a multimeter. Even where there is a significant reduction in the resistance of the winding, this is of little use unless you know the correct resistance. Accurate information of this type is not usually provided in component catalogues, but if you have another component of exactly the same type, a comparison of the readings obtained from the two components might show up a discrepancy.

Batteries
Testing batteries is one of those things that seems deceptively

simple. Just what constitutes an acceptable output voltage depends on the type of cell and the loading. With nickel-cadmium rechargeable cells and most other "high power" types there is relatively little variation in the output voltage during their lifespan. A voltage reduction of only about 10% or so usually indicates that this type of battery is largely discharged. Actually, most "high power" types, particularly nickel-cadmium cells, leave no doubt about when they reach exhaustion. The voltage drops very rapidly, in some cases giving an effect not much different to switching off the equipment!

Ordinary "dry" batteries are a different matter. They start off with a relatively high internal resistance, and this resistance steadily increases as the batteries discharge. Even with a voltage drop of over 20%, this type of battery can still be quite usable. This can lead to confusing results, with something like a 9 volt battery that produces a respectable 8 volts under test, but which does not seem to power its circuit properly in practice. This is usually the result of the circuit loading the battery quite heavily, while the multimeter draws no significant current from the battery. The easiest solution to this problem is to check the battery "in-situ" and with the equipment switched on, so that the reading obtained is the loaded battery voltage. Where this is not practical a load resistor can be added across the battery, as in Figure 25. This includes suggested load resistances for some popular batteries.

Switches

These are easily tested using a multimeter set to a resistance range to act as a continuity tester. It is just a matter of checking that the right tags (and only the right tags) are interconnected at each setting of the test component. This is a simple method of testing but an important one. Switches failing is not exactly a rarity, and I have had problems with poor reliability when using several types of switch. The smallest of the sub-miniature toggle types seem to be about the worst offenders. Also, the contact arrangements of some switches are less than obvious, and checking with a multimeter or continuity tester may be the only way of determining the details of the contact arrangement.

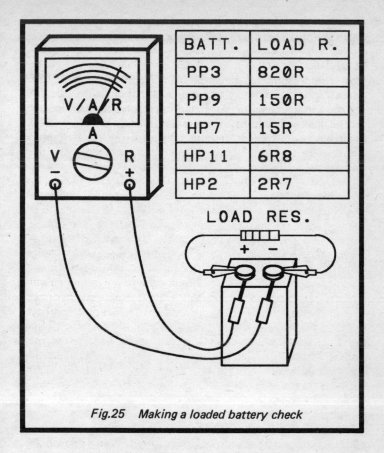

BATT.	LOAD R.
PP3	820R
PP9	150R
HP7	15R
HP11	6R8
HP2	2R7

LOAD RES.

Fig.25 Making a loaded battery check

Some projects specify the use of a "make before break" or "break before make" switch, and you may wish to determine whether or not a switch in the spares box is of the right type. The difference is that as the wiper switches from one contact to another, on a "make before break" switch the two contacts are momentarily short circuited together. With a "break before make" type the wiper is momentarily connected to neither contact. The brief short circuit between the contacts of a "make before break" type is easily detected using most multimeters (analogue types are best for this type of test). Its absence almost certainly indicates that the switch is of the "break before make" variety.

Finally

Most components can be given a reasonably thorough check-out using a multimeter, but one major group that can not are the various types of integrated circuits. These can mostly be checked satisfactorily using a multimeter, but only using in-circuit tests. These are the subject of the next chapter.

Chapter 3

CIRCUIT TESTING

Probably the main use for multimeters is making voltage and current checks on faulty circuits. It is only fair to point out that there is no instant method of learning this type of fault finding. There are some basic tests that virtually anyone can carry out, but much testing of this type requires a certain amount of technical knowledge. There is insufficient space available here for a complete course in electronics! However, details of some basic checks and voltage testing techniques are provided, and these should at least give a good idea of the basic approach used in this type of servicing. Having started you in the right direction, it is then up to you to assess faulty circuits, work out sensible test routines, and increase your technical knowledge where necessary.

Initial Tests

The first voltage tests on a piece of faulty equipment are to check that the supply is present. In the case of battery powered circuits this means first testing that approximately the correct voltage is present on the supply lines of the circuit board. If the voltage is present but conspicuously low, the obvious cause is a "flat" battery. Disconnecting the battery and measuring its loaded voltage (as described in the previous chapter) will confirm this, or will it? With voltage checks you have to learn the important distinction between reasoned conclusions and jumping to conclusions. The problem could be due to an exhausted battery, but it could just as easily be due to a fault in the circuit producing a very heavy current drain which is severely loading down what is a perfectly good battery. This second reason is really the more probable explanation, but a check of the supply current will soon show whether or not it is excessive.

It is standard practice to connect the current meter into the non-earthy supply lead, which is where it is less likely to have any major effect on the operation of the circuit. You can disconnect one terminal of the battery and insert the

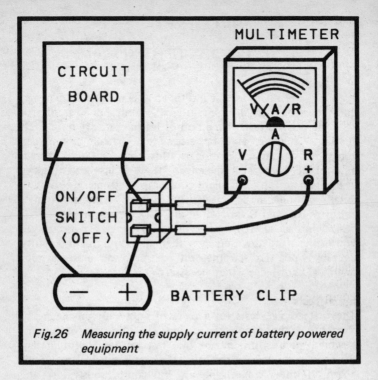

*Fig.26   Measuring the supply current of battery powered
equipment*

multimeter in the gap this produces, but it is usually easier to
use the method shown in Figure 26. Here the on/off switch is
set to the "off" position, and the multimeter is then connected across it with the correct polarity. Note that for positive
earth equipment the polarity of the multimeter would need
to be reversed. Another point to bear in mind is that the
current flow could be many times higher than the normal
current consumption of the circuit. Consequently, the meter
should be switched to a high current range, and it is probably
best to start with the highest range. If this fails to produce a
very large reading, the meter can be switched to a lower range
so that the current can be measured more accurately.

If a grossly excessive current flow is detected it is important to disconnect the meter at once so that the current is cut
off. Something in the circuit must be consuming this current,

and it will be in danger of seriously over-heating. This kind of fault is one of the most difficult types to deal with, since voltage tests are impossible. It is too risky to leave power connected to the circuit, but without it there are no voltages to read!

Continuity Testing

One approach to the problem is to use a continuity tester to search for accidental short circuits between tracks of the printed circuit board, broken tracks, or "dry" joints. A comprehensive check of this type can be a long process, but it will often bring results. I know of a company that sells large numbers of electronic kits, and which has a standard procedure for testing returned kits that have failed to work. The circuit boards are placed in a holder, and all the solder is then cleaned off the board. After they have been resoldered, about 90% of the kits operate perfectly. I have occasionally checked faulty projects for people, and the faults have almost invariably been bad joints, short circuits, and physically damaged components.

Before spending a large amount of time making detailed electronic checks on a project it is always a good idea to carry out a detailed physical inspection. In a fair percentage of cases this will bring the problem to light. Where the problem is essentially a physical rather than electronic one there may be no obvious signs of the fault. A magnifying glass can improve the chances of detecting physical faults, but will not always be successful. Cleaning of excess flux with one of the special cleaning sprays will further enhance the chances of success.

Where a physical inspection fails to produce results, continuity checking is the next stop. A multimeter set to a resistance range works quite well in this application, although it is less good than a good purpose-made continuity tester. Ideally the lowest resistance range should be used as this will not show continuity when there is a small but significant resistance between the test points. On the other hand, the lowest resistance range might be a little risky as it is almost certain to use fairly high test currents. My analogue multimeter, for example, has a maximum test current of about 150 milliamps on its lowest range. This is quite sufficient to damage many semiconductors, and continuity tests using this range could add faults to the circuit rather than help track down the existing ones!

Start by checking for short circuits between adjacent tracks and pads. These are most likely to occur where there is a very high track density, particularly where there are a lot of connections in a small area. This generally means in the vicinity of integrated circuits, multi-way connectors, or any components that have one or more rows of closely spaced terminals. Checking for broken tracks is just a matter of picking out the ends of tracks, and then checking for continuity between each pair of points. The nature of modern circuit boards is such that tracks tend to branch out all over the place, and it will often require several tests in order to fully check each one. Fortunately, provided the board is fixed in place (some "Blue Tak" will suffice for this) it is possible to completely check quite a large board in a reasonably short space of time. With the tracks on printed circuit boards seeming to get ever finer, this type of fault is considerably more common than it was a few years ago. Breaks in tracks where they meet pads seems to be the most common form of this fault.

Dry joints are a little more awkward to locate. Assuming that a physical inspection of the board does not show up any obvious candidates, it is a matter of checking for continuity between each soldered joint on one side of the board, and their corresponding leadout wires on the other side of the board. This type of testing is very much quicker and easier with fibreglass boards using a lightbox to permit the track pattern to be seen from the component side of the board. In fact a proper lightbox is by no means essential, and it is not difficult to improvise an arrangement that will enable the tracks to be seen from the wrong side of the board. Something to hold the board in place over a torch should suffice.

With the tracks visible from the component side of the board, test for continuity between pairs of leadout wires or pins that connect to the same track. This approach enables a lot of checks to be carried out easily and quickly. In fact this method "kills two birds with one stone" as it checks for both "dry" joints and breaks in the tracks. Of course, having found a lack of continuity, some more detailed checking will be needed in order to locate the exact fault, but it should take no more than a few seconds to complete the few additional continuity checks.

Mains Equipment

With mains power equipment, the first check is to ensure that the mains supply is actually reaching the equipment. However, **testing mains powered equipment is not something that can be recommended for beginners,** and some words of warning are in order here. Some ready-made equipment has one side of the mains connected to its chassis, and fault-finding on equipment of this type can be very dangerous. In a professional servicing establishment the mains supply for the work benches is derived via a large double-wound transformer. The point of this is that it is then impossible to sustain a severe electric shock to earth simply by touching the "live" side of the mains supply. The isolation provided by the mains transformer results in there being no "live" side of the mains to touch, but a severe shock could still be sustained by touching both sides of the 240 volt a.c. supply. The usual safety precaution, apart from proceeding very carefully, is to leave one hand in a pocket while servicing mains powered equipment. Although this may seem like an odd safety measure, it avoids the possibility of obtaining an electric shock from one hand to the other, which would take the electric current more or less straight through the heart. In fact with only one hand near the equipment under test it is very difficult to obtain an electric shock at all, although something like a shock through the end of one finger would be possible. This would be unpleasant, but would be unlikely to be dangerous.

For the amateur electronics enthusiast the extra protection provided by the mains isolation transformer will be absent. This is offset to some extent by the fact that most mains powered projects use an isolation and step-down transformer. The main circuit is both isolated from the mains supply, and almost invariably operates at low voltages that do not pose any risk. However, when making any measurements on the input side of the mains transformer there is a definite risk of receiving a powerful electric shock. If you must make measurements on the input side of a mains transformer, take very great care. If you proceed as carefully as you would if a mistake could be fatal, then you have the right idea. A mistake certainly could be fatal. Use test leads which have clip-on style test prods so that the one-handed approach can be adopted, and always use this method. Ordinary test prods are less than ideal for this type of testing, as they can easily slip and result in a minor catastrophe if the mains supply becomes short circuited.

Probably the best advice is to avoid tests on the mains supply as far as possible. In most cases they are completely avoidable. Consider the basic mains power supply circuit of Figure 27. If the circuit powered from the unit seems to be

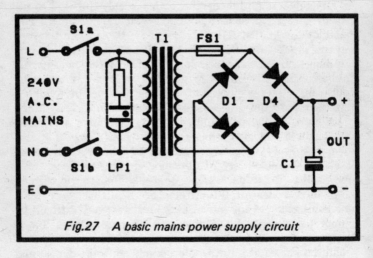

Fig.27   A basic mains power supply circuit

inactive, a sensible first test would be to **unplug the unit from the mains supply** and check for continuity between the "L" and "N" pins of the mains plug. With on/off switch S1 set to the "off" position there should be an immeasurably high resistance across these pins, but with S1 closed there should be a fairly low resistance. This is principally the resistance through the primary winding of mains transformer T1. The primary resistance of a mains transformer varies widely from one type to another, but it tends to be inversely related to the power rating of the component. For a small mains transformer something in the region of 2k would be typical, but for a high power type the resistance could easily be less than a hundredth of that figure.

Assuming that a fault is detected, and that with S1 closed there is not a suitable resistance present, further continuity checks could be used to narrow down the cause of the problem. As with any fault finding, it is best to adopt a logical approach to the problem. In this case, the obvious first check is to measure the resistance direct across the primary winding connections of T1. If a suitable resistance is present here, then the problem is in the wiring prior to T1, but if this test gives an open circuit indication, then T1 itself is faulty.

If T1 seems to be satisfactory, then the next check would be to determine whether the break in the wiring is in the "live" or "neutral" side of the mains wiring. This simply requires continuity checks to be made from the "live" and "neutral" pins of the mains plug to the relevant tags of T1. Be careful when making this type of continuity test, as a lack of continuity can sometimes prove to be just a poor connection from one of the test prods to the test point. Tags of mains transformers are often coated with some sort of clear lacquer, and excess flux is often to be found on soldered joints. Both tend to insulate the test points from the test prods, and the coatings may need to be scraped away in order to permit a reliable connection to be made. Heavy layers of oxide on tags and leadouts may also need to be cleaned away in order to permit a good connection to be made.

Having determined which side of the mains wiring contains the fault, further continuity tests should further narrow things down. If the fault was in the "live" side of the mains, a check across S1a would show whether or not this section of component had gone open circuit. The fuse in the mains plug is in this side of the mains, and this could also be checked. If neither of these checks shows a fault, then the problem is in the wiring from T1 to S1, or from S1 to the mains plug. Further continuity checks should determine which lead contains the break.

It is quite possible that a lack of activity from a mains powered project is not due to any fault on the mains side of the transformer. Indeed, it may not even be due to a fault in the power supply at all. In this example circuit there is a mains indicator neon connected across the primary winding of T1, and if this lights up when the unit is connected to the mains supply and switched on, then the mains supply is getting at least as far as LP1. The problem could still be due to a fault in the primary winding of T1. Alternatively, if T1 derives its power via LP1, then the problem could be due to a break in one of the wires from LP1 to T1. Again, continuity tests will soon track down this type of problem, and voltage checks are not required.

If everything on the input side of T1 seems to be satisfactory, then the output side must be checked. A couple of good initial tests would be to see if the correct a.c. output voltage is present across the secondary winding of T1, and if the d.c. output supply voltage is present across C1. These tests do, of course, require the unit to be plugged into the mains supply and switched on. Even when testing the low voltage sections of a mains power project, bear in mind that there is still some degree of risk involved. While testing a low voltage point in the circuit you could still accidentally touch a connection which is at the mains potential. The one-handed method should still be used, and great care should still be exercised. The use of sleeving and "boots" to insulate the mains connections is a good idea, and greatly aids safety when checking a mains powered project.

The absence of a suitable voltage across the secondary winding of T1 would suggest a faulty transformer. With fuse FS1 included in the circuit a lack of adequate voltage across the secondary would probably not be caused by an overload on the transformer. A serious overload would almost certainly "blow" the fuse. If the lack of output is due to a broken fuse, try fitting a new one. The chances are that the replacement will also "blow", and that the problem is due to a severe overload on the output. Replacing the fuse and checking to see if the replacement survives beyond switch-on is one safe way of checking for an overload. The fuse might survive, and it could be that the only problem was that the original fuse was faulty. You might prefer to make a few checks on the circuit before replacing the fuse. This means continuity checks in search of short circuits, or an obviously low load resistance. For example, the problem could be due to C1 (or a supply decoupling capacitor in the main circuit) going closed circuit, and a continuity check across the supply lines should reveal this fault. If signs of an excessive load on the output are apparent, do not bother replacing the fuse and switching on again until the source of the overloading has been revealed.

Finding a short circuit on the supply lines requires some careful thought or a lot of time. I would usually look carefully at the printed circuit board for points where the positive and negative supply rails run side by side. Normally printed circuit designers try to avoid this, but it is not always easily circumvented. In particular, some integrated circuits require the two supply rails to run to adjacent pins, and the supply tracks often have to run close together whether they meet up with a supply decoupling capacitor. In my experience any short circuits on the supply rails are virtually always due to excess solder blobs at one of these points on the board.

If this checking draws a blank, try testing any components which are connected across the supply rails. One lead of each component must be desoldered from the board so that it can be checked in isolation from other components across the supply rails. Things are a little more difficult with integrated circuits that are soldered direct to the circuit board. I avoid this problem by always using integrated circuit holders, except on the rare occasions when I use a special integrated circuit of some kind (usually a radio frequency device) where the manufacturers recommend direct connection to the board. With devices mounted in holders they can simply be unplugged, and a check then made to determine whether the short circuit is still present. With devices that are connected to the board, desoldering them is one way of checking to see if they are the cause of the problem. Even with an 8 pin DIL integrated circuit this can be a difficult and time consuming task, and with large types it can be very difficult indeed. It is probably best to exhaust all other possibilities before trying to disconnect large integrated circuits. It might be preferable to make a fine cut in one of the supply tracks leading to the suspect device. It can then be checked in isolation from the rest of the circuit, and the broken track can then be carefully soldered over with a short piece of tinned copper wire.

Bear in mind that just because a fairly high resistance reading is obtained when checking the load resistance of the power supply it does not automatically follow that there is no overload on the output. It indicates that there is no obvious overload, such as a short circuited supply decoupling capacitor, or a solder blob between printed circuit tracks carrying the supply rails. There could still be a fault in the main circuit that is causing it to draw too much current, but which does not manifest itself in the form of a low reading when a resistance check is made across the supply lines. This is simply because the resistance meter will be providing a test voltage that is almost certain to be just a fraction of the normal supply voltage. This lower voltage will almost invariably result in a greatly increased load resistance due to the voltage dependent resistance provided by most semiconductor devices. Also, unless you are careful about the polarity of the test prods, the test voltage may well be of the wrong polarity anyway.

Divided Voltages

The tests described so far have all been quite simple types that are more electrical than electronic in nature. Most voltage testing requires a slightly more technical approach, but in most cases it is just a matter of applying some fundamental mathematics to the problem. If you are lucky, the circuit diagram for the project will include test voltages so that the mathematics can be avoided. It is just a matter of comparing your test voltages with the voltages given on the diagram. Unless specified otherwise, test voltages are always given as potentials relative to the earth rail. With negative earth equipment the negative test prod connects to the earth rail and the positive prod is applied to the test points, but for positive earth equipment (which is pretty rare these days) the positive test prod is connected to earth.

Where test voltages are provided, it is important to know whether they are "real" voltages, or the potentials measured with a multimeter. In the case of measured voltages, it is important to know whether they were obtained using a 20k/volt instrument or a high input resistance instrument such as a digital multimeter. Most test voltages seem to be those to be expected when using a 20k/volt instrument, but I have encountered some that are the theoretical voltages or the levels to be expected using a high resistance voltmeter (which in most cases will not be significantly different to the theoretical voltages). If you are not using the same type of meter that was used for the original voltage checks, then you will need to bear in mind the different loading levels when testing low current parts of the circuit.

Estimating Voltages

When dealing with home constructed projects you will not usually have test voltages of any type marked on circuit diagrams. In some cases this may leave you in the position where there is no certain way of making a reasonably accurate estimation of a test voltage. This is most likely to occur where a circuit utilizes a special integrated circuit, and unless you have detailed data on the chip concerned, there is no way of telling what sort of voltage should be present at many of its pins. In most cases though, a little mathematics will permit the circuit voltages to be estimated with reasonable accuracy.

The examples given in Chapter 1 when discussing multimeter loading give a good idea of the general way in which voltage estimations have to be handed. As you may recall, in that example there was a potential divider connected across the 10 volt supply. As the two resistors were of equal value, the voltage at their junction was half the supply voltage, or 5 volts in other words. Estimating circuit voltages is not always quite as straightforward as this, but simple bias networks of this type are far from uncommon in linear circuits. Much testing is therefore just a matter of checking that strategic points in a circuit are at something close to half the supply potential.

Sometimes the method of biasing will not make the half supply voltage bias level quite so obvious, and Figure 28 shows a less clear-cut example. Here there are three resistors in the bias network, but the circuit is not really much different to our earlier example. R2 and R3 are the bias resistor circuit, and R1 plus C1 form a so-called "hum" filter. This name is derived from the fact that it is intended to filter out

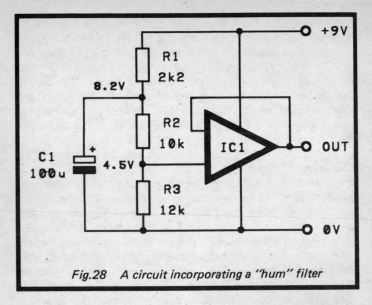

Fig.28   A circuit incorporating a "hum" filter

any mains "hum" on the supply lines, and prevent it from being coupled to the input of the amplifier via the bias circuit. In practice these filters are often included for other reasons, such as combatting low frequency instability ("motor boating") due to feedback through the supply lines.

Sometimes the "hum" filter resistor will have such a low resistance compared to the bias resistors that the voltage drop across it will be negligible. This is not the case here, and the bias circuit has been designed so that R1 effectively forms part of the bias network. The upper resistance of the potential divider is the 12.2k provided by the series resistance of R1 plus R2, while the 12k of R3 forms the lower section of the network. This gives a slight imbalance, but not really enough to worry about. The voltage at the junction of R2 and R3 should be very close to half the supply voltage (or in the region of 4.5 volts in other words).

It is not difficult to work out the voltage at the junction of R1 and R2. Basic electronic theory tells us that the voltage across each resistor in the potential divider chain is governed by the supply voltage, and each resistor's proportion of the total resistance in the network. In order to work out the voltage across any resistor in a divider network it is just a matter of working out what fraction of the total resistance it provides, and then multiplying the supply potential by this figure. In this case the total resistance through the divider network is clearly 24.2k (2.2k + 10k + 12k = 24.2k). Dividing the 2.2k of R1 by the 24.2k total gives an answer of 0.091. Multiplying this by the supply potential of 9 volts gives a voltage drop across R1 of 0.82 volts. This gives a potential of approximately 8.2 volts at the junction of R1 and R2.

It is not usually necessary to work things out this accurately. A little mental arithmetic will give an approximate value for the total resistance through the resistor network, and it should then be fairly easy to roughly estimate the proportion of this value accounted for by any resistor in the network. In this example there is obviously about 24k through the resistor chain, and R1 clearly represents a little under one-tenth of this value. This equates to a little under 1 volt across R1, and a little over 8 volts at the junction of R1 and R2. Most circuit voltages are subject to large tolerances. This is not just due to the tolerances of resistors, and other factors can have a greater influence. With battery powered equipment for example, a supposedly 9 volt supply voltage is quite likely to substantially depart from its nominal level. In fact it is a good idea to measure the actual supply voltage so that any large discrepancy can be allowed for when assessing voltage readings.

Apart from the fact that actual circuit voltages are likely to differ significantly from the theoretical levels, voltages do not need to be measured with great accuracy as faults almost invariably produce large voltage errors, or none at all. Consequently they will normally be quite obvious from a voltage check, or will be undetectable by this method. An obvious fault would be something such as zero volts being produced at the junction of both R1-R2 and R2-R3 in the circuit of Figure 28. This would indicate that C1 had gone closed circuit, or that R1 had become open circuit. Alternatively, a solder blob might be short circuiting C1, or a "dry" joint could result in R1 not being connected into circuit properly. Note that the fault could not be due to faults in R2, R3, or the integrated circuit. Faults in one of these could produce zero volts at the junction of R2 and R3, but not at the junction of R1 and R2.

Remember that where an amplifier or other circuit is biased from a potential divider circuit, it might significantly load the bias network. With circuits that are based on operational amplifiers the degree of loading is normally insignificant. Discrete circuits are normally designed so that any loading placed on the bias network will be minimal, at less than about 10%. However, in some cases larger loading occurs, and the multimeter could further increase the loading. Some allowance for this therefore has to be made when testing discrete circuits, especially those where the bias resistor values are quite high.

No Change

As an example of a fault that would be undetectable by voltage checks, consider the circuit of Figure 29. This has

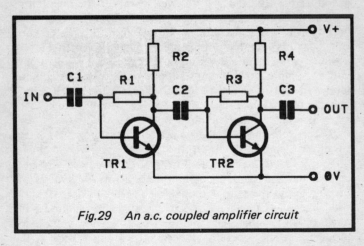

Fig.29   An a.c. coupled amplifier circuit

two common emitter amplifiers with inter-stage coupling provided by C2. Suppose that C2 became disconnected due to a "dry" joint or that is became open circuit. Obviously the amplifier would no longer work as no signal would be coupled from the output of TR1 to the input of TR2. On the other hand, there is nothing to produce any voltage changes in the circuit. The purpose of C2 is to effectively couple the a.c. audio signal through from one stage to the next while blocking the d.c. level at the collector of TR1 from reaching the base of TR2. A fault of the type described above will prevent the a.c. audio signal from being coupled through the circuit, but it will not upset the d.c. bias levels.

A multimeter can be used to detect most types of fault, but it will not always prove to be effective. If a set of voltage checks fails to bring the fault to light, then a different approach and possibly different test equipment must be used. A fault of this type is most easily tracked down using a signal injector or tracer. Improvised techniques can often be quite fast and effective. A popular ploy when testing amplifiers is to use the "finger dabbing" technique. This relies on the fact that your body will tend to pick up substantial amounts of mains "hum" and other electrical noise. Touching a finger-tip onto any moderately sensitive point in an amplifier will therefore give a crude signal injection action with a lot of general noise being produced at the output of the circuit. In this case, touching the base of TR2 would produce a noise signal from the output, but touching the base of TR1 would not (or more probably it would produce a very weak output signal due to stray coupling through the circuit).

I suppose that this fault could be detected using only a multimeter. With all the bias voltages correct, the obvious cause of no output is a break somewhere in the signal path rather than something like a faulty transistor or bias resistor. Continuity checks could be used to test for any "dry" joints or broken printed circuit tracks. Provided the coupling capacitors are reasonably high in value (which would normally be the case) there should be little difficulty in desoldering one leadout wire of each one, and then giving them a check using the system described in the previous chapter.

Bias Voltage

The circuit of Figure 29 is one where it might appear to be quite difficult, or even impossible, to make realistic estimates of the bias voltages. There are no potential divider circuits of the type used in the circuit of Figure 28 and described previously. However, an educated guess of the bias levels can be made. The voltages at the collectors of TR1 and TR2 are almost certain to be something not too far removed from half the supply voltage. This is simply because it is normal to design linear circuits this way. A half supply voltage bias level enables the highest possible signal level to be handled before the onset of clipping and serious distortion. Even at low signal levels it usually provides better distortion performance than a bias level that is well offset from the half supply voltage level. With a bias circuit of the type used in this circuit the bias voltages can not be set very accurately, and anything from around 30% to 70% of the supply voltage would be perfectly acceptable as a test voltage.

Estimating the voltages at the bases of TR1 and TR2 is much easier. Assuming these are silicon devices, they require a base bias of about 0.6 volts before they start to conduct, but they reach saturation at a base voltage only marginally higher than this. The base voltages should therefore be close to 0.6 volts. However, the base bias resistors are likely to be quite high in value, and could each be several megohms. A digital multimeter would probably give quite an accurate reading, but the combination of low voltage and high source resistance would defeat an ordinary analogue multimeter. It would probably be impossible to get more than a very slight deflection of the meter's pointer.

Current Tracing

Sometimes when fault finding it is helpful to know where the supply current is going. This mainly applies to a situation where the supply current is far removed from its correct level, and you wish to know how this current is divided up amongst the various stages in a circuit. With an amplifier circuit of the type shown in Figure 29, measuring the voltage across each load resistor will enable the supply current to be calculated. Suppose that the voltage at the collector of TR1 is 4.3 volts, and that the actual supply voltage is 9.1 volts. This gives 4.8 volts across R2 (9.1 − 4.3 = 4.8 volts). From Ohm's Law we know that current is equal to voltage divided by resistance, and assuming a typical value of 4k7 for R2, this gives 4.8/4.7, or 1.02 milliamps.

Note that because the resistance is in kilohms rather than ohms, the answer is in milliamps and not amps. Using microamps in a calculation of this type gives an answer in megohms incidentally.

With this type of testing it is not really necessary to reach for the calculator and make exact calculations, and in this example it is quite obvious that the current flow is slightly over 1 milliamp. This type of checking is not always applicable, as there may be no convenient resistors in the supply lines to facilitate the voltage measurements. There is not usually a problem with discrete component circuits, but integrated circuits tend to be less accommodating. With linear types they may well be fed from the supply lines via a series resistor that forms part of a decoupling network, and measuring the voltage drop across these resistors enables the current flow at various points in the circuit to be calculated. Logic devices are less accommodating, and this system is unusable with these.

This system can be applied to other current measurements. As a typical example, suppose that you want to know the current flow through a light emitting diode. These are almost invariably fed via a current limiting resistor, and measuring the voltage across this resistor enables the current flow to be calculated.

With tests of this type you need to keep in mind the fact that the accuracy of the calculated current is dependent on the resistance figure being accurate. A quick check of the resistor used in this test is always a worthwhile precaution.

Which Fault?

While not all faults produce voltage changes in a circuit, quite a large proportion do seem to do so. With our open circuit capacitor there are no voltage changes, but if the capacitor went closed circuit there would be definite voltage changes. R2 would provide a large bias current to TR2 that would bias it hard into conduction. Its collector voltage would fall to virtually zero, and the signal path would be blocked.

This is the type of fault where it is much easier to jump to conclusions than to correctly diagnose the fault. Ignoring such things as "dry" joints and broken printed circuit tracks, there are a number of possible causes for TR2 having a very low collector voltage. The problem could be that TR2 has gone closed circuit from its collector to emitter terminals, R4 could have gone high in value, R3 could have gone low in value, or C2 could have gone closed circuit. One way of detecting the exact nature of the fault would be to test all the suspect components, and sometimes this is indeed the only way forward. It can often be worthwhile making further voltage checks though, with the results being carefully noted down. In this case the base voltage of TR2 and the collector voltage of TR1 would be very revealing.

The base voltage of TR2 would normally give quite a low reading, especially if the measurement was made using an ordinary analogue multimeter. With R2 providing a strong bias the situation is very different, and using any multimeter a rather high reading of about 0.7 volts would be obtained. This could be due to a fault in R3, and would not definitely point to a fault in C2. However, the same is not true of the voltage at the collector of TR1. This should be at about half the supply potential, but it too would be at about 0.7 volts. The fact that the fault was affecting both stages of the amplifier would be a strong indication that inter-stage capacitor was not providing any d.c. blocking. TR1's collector and TR2's base at precisely the same potential would tend to confirm that the fault was C2 having gone closed circuit. The precision of digital instruments is useful for this type of testing as it makes it quite clear when two supposedly unconnected test points are at precisely the same voltage rather than simply at similar voltages. The fact that two supposedly unconnected points in a circuit are at exactly the same voltage does not necessarily mean that there is a short circuit between them. On the other hand, it is by far the most likely explanation.

Oscillators

Voltage checks are normally made with the circuit under test as inactive as possible. With a hi-fi amplifier for instance, there would be no input signal applied to the unit while it was being checked. The reason for this is that signals can affect the voltages in a circuit, and with digital multimeters can give rather unpredictable and highly unreliable results.

This factor makes d.c. voltage checks on oscillators of relatively little value. There may be some true d.c. bias levels in an oscillator circuit, but in many cases all the points in the circuit (apart from the supply rails) will be at varying d.c. voltages. The measured voltages on a fully operational stage may bear little similarity to the calculated d.c. bias levels, and the multimeter used to make the measurement might give erroneous readings anyway. It might be worthwhile checking for a lack of supply voltage, or checking for other obvious signs of a fault, but d.c. voltage checks on oscillators are likely to be very unrevealing.

The purpose of an oscillator is to generate an a.c. or varying d.c. signal, and a more useful test is to check for the presence or absence of an output signal. This is the sort of thing that requires an oscilloscope or a frequency meter if it is to be done properly. Checks can then be made to determine if the output frequency and wave shape are correct. With a multimeter it is only possible to check for the presence or absence of some sort of signal. The frequency and wave shape of the signal remain unknown quantities, although some idea of the signal level will be obtained.

Due to the very simple a.c. voltage measuring circuits used in most multimeters, it is very easy to obtain misleading results when checking for an a.c. output signal. Analogue multimeters use an a.c. voltage measuring circuit that is usually something along the lines of Figure 30. This is just a basic half wave rectifier incorporated into a d.c. voltage measuring circuit. The main point to note is that the circuit will respond to a d.c. input signal of the correct polarity (but it will not respond to d.c. input signal of reverse polarity). This is not a very satisfactory state of affairs in that there is no certain way of knowing whether the instrument is measuring a true a.c. voltage level, a d.c. voltage, or a mixture of the two. A d.c. blocking capacitor in the circuit would greatly improve matters, but I have encountered few analogue multimeters that include such a component.

Digital multimeters use a substantially more sophisticated a.c. voltage measuring arrangement of the type outlined in Figure 31. Here a precision fullwave rectifier and smoothing

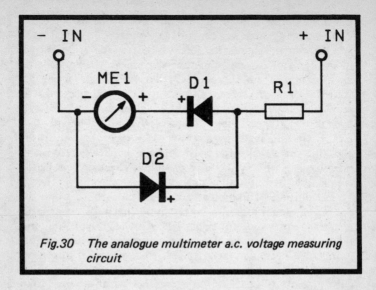

Fig.30   The analogue multimeter a.c. voltage measuring circuit

circuit provide an accurate a.c. to d.c. conversion, but this arrangement is no better than the simple system used in analogue instruments. It still responds to d.c. signals as well as a.c. types, and will in fact respond to d.c. signals of either polarity. Again, a d.c. blocking capacitor at the input can greatly improve matters, and such a component is often included in digital multimeters. It is not always present though. It is easy enough to tell whether or not your multimeter includes a d.c. blocking capacitor on the a.c. voltage ranges, and it is just a matter of using it to measure a d.c. voltage. Try connecting the multimeter with both polarities. If either test gives a steady reading, the instrument does not include d.c. blocking.

If a suitable capacitor is not incorporated in your multimeter, then an external component can be added when making tests where d.c. potentials might give misleading results. Tests on the mains supply and transformers will not usually give any problems, but tests on oscillators are a different matter. The value to use for the capacitor depends on the lowest frequency that must be accommodated, and on the input resistance of the multimeter. With digital types a fairly low

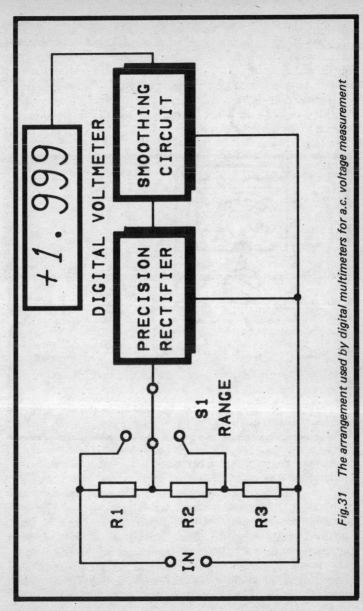

Fig.31   The arrangement used by digital multimeters for a.c. voltage measurement

value of about 100nF should give a very low cutoff frequency. The much lower input resistance of analogue multimeters necessitates the use of a substantially higher value in order to obtain a reasonably low cutoff frequency. This means having to use an electrolytic component, or a physically large and expensive non-electrolytic type. This is possibly why d.c. blocking capacitors are not normally included as integral parts of analogue multimeters.

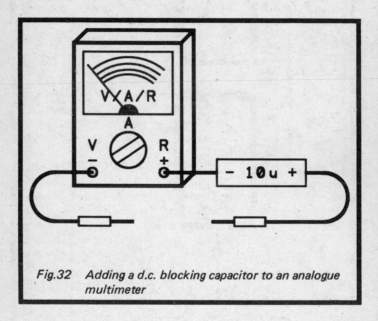

Fig.32   Adding a d.c. blocking capacitor to an analogue multimeter

Assuming that measurements are to be made on negative earth equipment, and that the negative test prod will be connected to earth, the arrangement of Figure 32 can be used. A 10 microfarad capacitor will give a reasonably low cutoff frequency on any range of the instrument, including the low voltage ranges which are presumably the ones that will be used for the types of check that will require the additional capacitor. It should certainly give good results right down to the lower end of the audio spectrum (about 20 to 30 Hertz). The working voltage of the capacitor needs to be higher than any d.c. voltage that will need to be blocked, and also needs to be higher than the maximum peak to peak voltage of any a.c. signal that it will pass. For tests on low voltage circuits (up to about a 24 volt supply) a 25 volt capacitor should therefore be suitable. Such an arrangement is only suitable for low voltage a.c. tests, and the capacitor must not be included when making high voltage checks.

If a miniature capacitor is used it might be possible to build it into a test prod or its plug, which would be a very neat and convenient means of accommodating this component. Alternatively, it could be fitted into a miniature plastic case and wired "in-line".

Response Limitations

As pointed out in Chapter 1, multimeters almost always have very limited bandwidths on their a.c. voltage ranges. If the specification sheet for your instrument does not specify the upper limit of its response, a few checks on some a.c. signal sources should give some idea of its useful frequency range. Most types are suitable for operation at low and middle audio frequencies, but few digital types are much use beyond this. Analogue types can usually operate over the full audio range, and in some cases can operate well beyond the upper limit of the audio range and into the radio frequency spectrum. Obviously there is no point in trying to detect the output from something like a 2MHz crystal oscillator using a digital multimeter which has a response that rolls-off above about 500Hz. It would probably not be able to detect a signal at 2MHz at all.

With an audio oscillator circuit such as the standard 555 astable shown in Figure 33 there should be no difficulty in detecting the a.c. output signal with any multimeter. The output signal direct from IC1 is actually a pulsing d.c. type rather than a true a.c. signal, and a d.c. blocking capacitor is needed somewhere in the system in order to give a reliable measurement. The peak to peak output voltage from this oscillator (and many other types) is virtually equal to the supply voltage. Dividing this by 2.8 gives an approximate r.m.s. (root mean square) output voltage, which is what the a.c. voltage scale of a multimeter is normally calibrated to

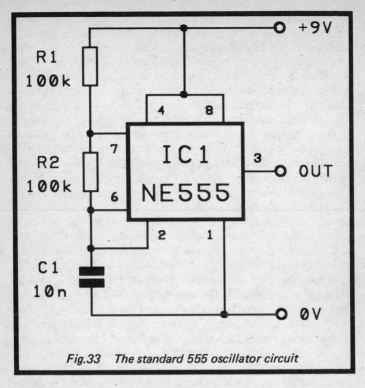

Fig.33   The standard 555 oscillator circuit

read.   However, this calculation assumes that the output signal is a sinewave type.   Many oscillator circuits, including the 555 type of Figure 33, provide an output waveform that does not even roughly approximate to a sinewave.   Although the calculated r.m.s. output voltage from the circuit of Figure 33 is around 3.2 volts (9 divided by 2.8 = 3.2), the measured output voltage could depart significantly from this.   With an output signal having a very high or very low mark-space ratio the a.c. output level could be very low.

In practice, it is generally good enough just to test for any output from an oscillator, without needing to have detailed information on the nature of the output signal.   Bear in mind though, that this simple go/no go form of testing is not 100% reliable, and that the oscillator could be providing an unsuitable output signal (wrong frequency, incorrect wave shape, or whatever). If you have an oscilloscope it is better suited to this type of testing than is a multimeter.

When there is no output signal from a relaxation oscillator (such as a 555 astable circuit), d.c. voltage tests will often reveal the fault. With a 555 astable circuit the timing capacitor (C1) is charged to two-thirds of the supply voltage via R1 and R2, and then discharged to one-third of the supply voltage by way of R2 and an internal switching transistor of IC1. C1 then starts to charge again, and this process continues indefinitely. The output of IC1 goes high during the charge period, and low while C1 is discharging. The d.c. output level from IC1 therefore gives some clue as to the possible fault.

If the output was continuously high for instance, this would strongly suggest that C1 was not being charged, which should be confirmed by a voltage check across this component. Resistance and continuity tests would soon determine whether it was R1, R2, or C1 that was at fault, or some other cause such as a broken printed circuit track. If everything checked out alright, then this would tend to indicate that IC1 was faulty, or perhaps that an accidental short circuit between pins 3 and 4 was causing its output to be short circuited to the positive supply rail. A point worth keeping in mind is that if a fault causes strong loading of the supply voltage due to an excessive current drain, the problem is much more likely to be in the output section of the circuit than at the input. A device in the circuit getting much hotter than normal is usually a good pointer to the cause of the problem.

R.F. Oscillators

Radio frequency oscillators are more difficult to test as their output signal will often be at a frequency that can not be detected using the a.c. voltage range of a multimeter. One solution to the problem, and quite a good one, is to build an r.f. probe that will convert an r.f. input signal to a d.c. output signal that should be measurable using any multimeter. Something as basic as the rectifier and smoothing circuit of Figure 34 will usually suffice. When used with my digital and analogue multimeters on their most sensitive d.c. ranges it permitted a.c. signals of moderate amplitude to be detected

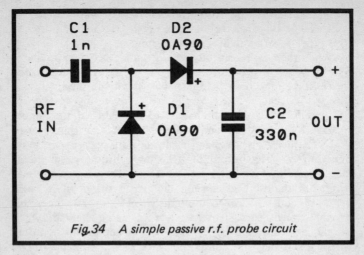

Fig.34   A simple passive r.f. probe circuit

at frequencies of more than 50MHz. Their a.c. voltage ranges are useless at one-thousandth of this figure.

This is a purely passive circuit, and it will load the circuit under investigation quite heavily. This means that a signal may be more readily detected in a low impedance part of the circuit than in a high impedance type (such as direct across a tuned circuit). The signal level might be smaller in a low impedance part of the circuit, but it will usually be readily detectable. When using a simple probe of this type on a high impedance part of the test circuit there is a danger that it will load the circuit to the point when it stifles oscillation and gives a misleading indication. It is important to realise that a simple r.f. measuring circuit of this type will not provide an accurate indication of signal voltages. It simply indicates the presence or absence of an r.f. input signal, and gives a rough indication of the signal strength.

Radio frequency probes are normally constructed along the lines shown in Figure 35. The point of this method is that it provides a virtually lead-less connection at the input where the high signal frequencies make long leads undesirable. There is a long lead at the output, but this is only carrying a d.c. signal, and a long cable is quite acceptable. Note that D1 and D2 are germanium diodes, and are much more vulnerable to

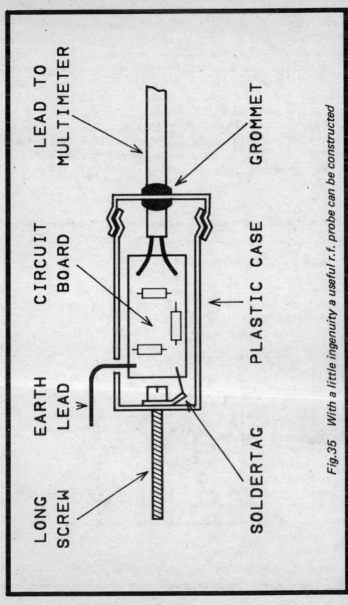

LONG SCREW · EARTH LEAD · CIRCUIT BOARD · LEAD TO MULTIMETER · GROMMET · PLASTIC CASE · SOLDERTAG

Fig.35   With a little ingenuity a useful r.f. probe can be constructed

93

heat damage than silicon diodes. Due care should therefore be exercised when making connections to them.

An alternative to using an r.f. probe to detect high frequency oscillations is to block oscillation, and check for any change in the d.c. bias levels. As explained previously, the d.c. levels are usually completely different to those calculated from d.c. theory. This is simply because the circuit is not under steady d.c. conditions, but will usually be oscillating strongly and almost certainly non-symmetrically. Some parts of the circuit will not be at steady d.c. levels, and those that are will almost certainly have their average potentials shifted from their normal levels by the lack of symmetry in the output signal.

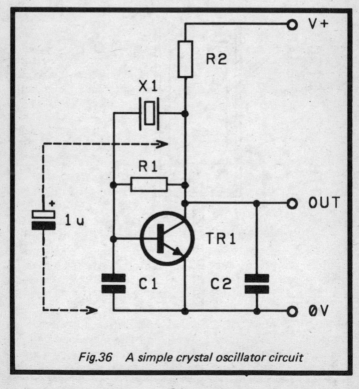

Fig.36   A simple crystal oscillator circuit

As an example of how this system can operate, consider the crystal oscillator circuit of Figure 36. One way of stopping the circuit from oscillating is to disconnect the crystal, and if it is a plug-in type, then unplugging it represents an easy way of blocking oscillation. If it is a wire-ended type which is soldered into circuit, disconnecting the crystal would unnecessarily risk damaging it. A simple alternative would be to wire a high value capacitor across C2 in order to suppress oscillation without affecting the bias levels. A value of about 1 microfarad should suffice, and this component can simply be wired into circuit temporarily using crocodile clip leads. With an oscillator that is functioning, this test will normally produce a d.c. shift of about 0.5 to 2 volts at a strategic point in the circuit. In this case, the collector of TR1 is the obvious point to make the voltage measurements.

Audio Measurements
Much audio measuring requires the use of sensitive equipment to detect quite low level signals. This includes things such as the measurement of signal to noise ratio and the voltage gain of preamplifiers. However, there are some simple but useful tests that can be made using a suitable multimeter, but only with the aid of a signal generator. About the most simple of these measurements is audio output power. In fact the multimeter is used to measure the a.c. output voltage of an amplifier, and some simple mathematics are used to convert this into a figure for output power in watts r.m.s.

This is something that needs to be done carefully if a worthwhile result is to be obtained. The amplifier should be loaded while this test is made, and a high power resistor having a value equal to the normal load resistance of the amplifier is the most suitable form of load. A loudspeaker of the correct impedance could be used, but would have two drawbacks. One is merely that the sound it would produce could be a little ear-splitting, as a continuous loud tone is not the most pleasant of sounds. The more major drawback is that the actual impedance of a loudspeaker is often well removed from its nominal figure. In fact most loudspeakers have an impedance that fluctuates considerably as the input frequency is varied over the audio frequency range. At the frequency used for the test the loudspeaker could have the correct impedance, but an error of −50% to +100% could easily occur. Clearly this would seriously degrade the value of the output power measurement.

Maximum audio output power is normally measured with the output signal level just on the verge of clipping. In the absence of audio distortion measuring equipment or an oscilloscope, the output of the amplifier can be monitored with a pair of headphones fed from the output of the amplifier via a resistor of about 1k in value (or about 10k for medium—high impedance headphones). This series resistor performs two functions. Firstly, it ensures that the strong output from the amplifier does not damage the headphones. Secondly, it gives moderate volume from the phones, which makes detecting the increased distortion at the onset of clipping as easy as possible. Actually, most modern amplifiers provide "hard" clipping, and using a sinewave test signal, the change in the sound quality as clipping starts is usually very obvious. Figure 37 gives details of the suggested output power test setup.

The output level should be as high as possible without this increased distortion becoming evident. Note that for frequency response and output power measurements the test signal should always be a reasonably pure sinewave signal. It is not necessary to use an ultra-low distortion signal generator though.

Output power is equal to the square of the output voltage divided by the load impedance. For example, with an output voltage of 10.6 volts r.m.s., squaring this figure gives an answer of 112.36. Assuming a normal 8 ohm load impedance, dividing this figure by 8 gives an output power of 14.045 watts.

Testing the frequency response of a power amplifier is equally straightforward. In fact most preamplifiers can provide a fairly high output level, and will provide high enough readings on most multimeters to permit accurate frequency response tests to be carried out. This type of testing is useful when checking tone control circuits and equalised preamplifiers.

The basic setup is exactly the same as for measuring output power, but in the case of a preamplifier the output load resistor

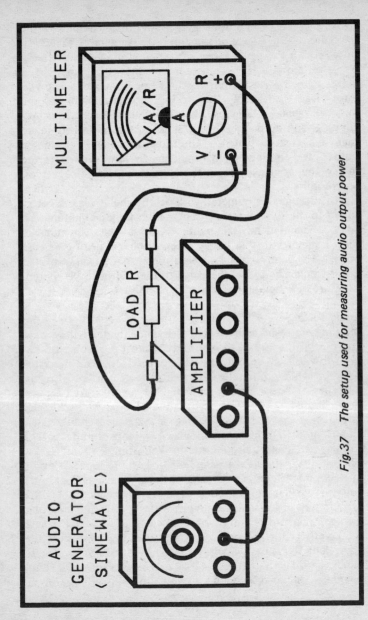

Fig.37 The setup used for measuring audio output power

is unnecessary. The output level should be set well below the maximum output level of the amplifier (preferably at −20dB or less) with the signal generator set to a middle audio frequency of around 1kHz. Remember that there may be a considerable rise in the response at some frequencies, and you must leave sufficient "headroom" to accommodate the boosted signal. Otherwise the amplifier will be driven into clipping, and output readings will then be substantially lower than the correct figures. On the other hand, setting the output level too low might result in very low readings on the meter and poor accuracy. It is a matter of finding a good compromise.

An analogue multimeter with its decibel scales is better suited to this type of testing than are most digital multimeters. Also, as pointed out in Chapter 1, most digital instruments offer a bandwidth that barely reaches the middle of the audio range. These are alright for measuring output power, provided a test frequency within the range of the multimeter is chosen. They are of little use for frequency response testing.

Logic Testing

Multimeters seem to be regarded less highly than they were (say) ten to twenty years ago, and the most probable explanation for this is the growth of digital electronics over this period. While multimeters are well suited to testing virtually all types of linear circuit, with logic types they are of much more limited value. They can be used for basic checks such as checking that the supply voltage is reaching each integrated circuit on the printed circuit board, plus continuity checks for accidental short circuits and broken printed circuit tracks. They can also be used to ascertain that static inputs/outputs in the circuit are at the correct logic levels, and at legal voltages. What constitutes a legal voltage depends on the logic family in use and the supply voltage, but for 5 volt TTL devices logic 0 means 0.8 volts or less, and logic 1 means 2 to 5 volts. For the popular 4000 series CMOS devices the equivalent figures are 1 volt or less and 4 to 5 volts. These increase to 4 volts or less and 11 to 15 volts for 4000 series integrated circuits used with a 15 volt supply.

This is all reasonably useful, but logic circuits are very much about pulse signals and not static levels. With constructors who build a lot of digital circuits it tends to be the logic probe rather than the multimeter that they turn to when a circuit fails to operate properly. It would be misleading for me to suggest that a multimeter is better suited than a logic probe to logic circuit testing.

Other useful tests can be made on logic circuits using a multimeter by making use of the fact that an analogue multimeter will register the average voltage of a medium to high frequency pulse signal. Digital multimeters mostly do not response to pulse signals in the same way, but the addition of a simple smoothing circuit (as in Figure 38) seems to convert them to the desired action. The voltage drop through the series resistor obviously affects readings to some extent, but the very high input resistance of digital multimeters means that the effect of this resistor should be insignificant.

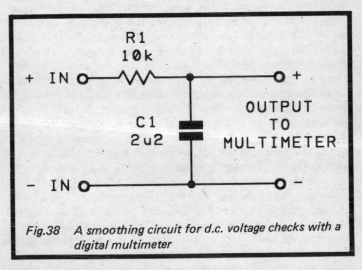

Fig.38   A smoothing circuit for d.c. voltage checks with a
digital multimeter

As a simple example of how this average voltage technique can be used, we will assume that a binary divider chain is to be checked. The output voltage from a divide by two flip/flop circuit has a perfect 1 : 1 mark space ratio, and so the average output voltage is half the supply voltage. This is a slight over-simplification in that many logic circuits have non-symmetrical output signals where the logic 0 output level tends to be very close to 0 volts, but the logic 1 level can fall well short of the positive supply voltage. This lack of symmetry is more notice-able with TTL devices than with 4000 series CMOS types. What it means in practice is that the average output voltage will often be slightly lower than that suggested by a simple calculation based on the mark-space ratio of the test signal and the supply voltage.

In our binary divider example we would expect the output from each stage to be about half the supply voltage, but possibly somewhat less (about 2 volts) for a circuit based on TTL devices. A voltage much higher or lower than the expected voltage would probably indicate that the output from that divider was static. This could be confirmed by testing the output from subsequent dividers, which should also have static outputs as they would not be receiving any input pulses. This type of testing is far from perfect, and what seems like a valid pulse signal could be a static signal at an invalid level, or a pulse signal that has not undergone any division. Faults of this type seem to be quite rare in practice though, and this type of testing is usually quite effective.

Obviously the pulse signal will not always have a convenient 1 to 1 mark-space ratio. If the signal is high for a greater proportion of the time, then the average output voltage is higher; if it is low for a greater proportion of the time then the average output voltage is lower. This type of testing is less valuable with mark-space ratios that are well away from 1 to 1, as a static logic 0 level would be indistinguishable from a pulse signal that is low for 99% of the time. Voltage checks can still be useful, as a voltage reading that should be very low might produce a static logic 1 level instead of a logic 0 type, and the voltage test would then clearly indicate the fault. Where this type of testing is of least use is where there are brief and intermittent pulses. A voltage check would detect the wrong logic level under stand-by conditions, but it would not detect the much more likely problem of missing pulses. An oscilloscope or logic probe are required for this type of logic testing.

Notes

Please note following is a list of other titles that are available in our range of Radio, Electronics and Computer Books.

These should be available from all good Booksellers, Radio Component Dealers and Mail Order Companies.

However, should you experience difficulty in obtaining any title in your area, then please write directly to the publisher enclosing payment to cover the cost of the book plus adequate postage.

If you would like a complete catalogue of our entire range of Radio, Electronics and Computer Books then please send a Stamped Addressed Envelope to:

BERNARD BABANI (publishing) LTD
THE GRAMPIANS
SHEPHERDS BUSH ROAD
LONDON W6 7NF
ENGLAND

160	Coil Design and Construction Manual	£2.50
205	Hi-Fi Loudspeaker Enclosures	£2.95
208	Practical Stereo & Quadrophony Handbook	£0.75
214	Audio Enthusiast's Handbook	£0.85
219	Solid State Novelty Projects	£0.85
220	Build Your Own Solid State Hi-Fi and Audio Accessories	£0.85
222	Solid State Short Wave Receivers for Beginners	£2.95
225	A Practical Introduction to Digital ICs	£2.50
226	How to Build Advanced Short Wave Receivers	£2.95
227	Beginners Guide to Building Electronic Projects	£1.95
228	Essential Theory for the Electronics Hobbyist	£2.50
BP2	Handbook of Radio, TV, Industrial and Transmitting Tube and Valve Equivalents	£0.60
BP6	Engineer's & Machinist's Reference Tables	£1.25
BP7	Radio & Electronic Colour Codes Data Chart	£0.95
BP27	Chart of Radio, Electronic, Semiconductor and Logic Symbols	£0.95
BP28	Resistor Selection Handbook	£0.60
BP29	Major Solid State Audio Hi-Fi Construction Projects	£0.85
BP33	Electronic Calculator Users Handbook	£1.50
BP36	50 Circuits Using Germanium Silicon and Zener Diodes	£1.50
BP37	50 Projects Using Relays, SCRs and TRIACs	£2.95
BP39	50 (FET) Field Effect Transistor Projects	£2.95
BP42	50 Simple LED Circuits	£1.95
BP44	IC 555 Projects	£2.95
BP45	Projects in Opto-Electronics	£1.95
BP48	Electronic Projects for Beginners	£1.95
BP49	Popular Electronic Projects	£2.50
BP53	Practical Electronics Calculations and Formulae	£3.95
BP54	Your Electronic Calculator & Your Money	£1.35
BP56	Electronic Security Devices	£2.50
BP58	50 Circuits Using 7400 Series IC's	£2.50
BP62	The Simple Electronic Circuit & Components (Elements of Electronics — Book 1)	£3.50
BP63	Alternating Current Theory (Elements of Electronics — Book 2)	£3.50
BP64	Semiconductor Technology (Elements of Electronics — Book 3)	£3.50
BP66	Beginners Guide to Microprocessors and Computing	£1.95
BP68	Choosing and Using Your Hi-Fi	£1.65
BP69	Electronic Games	£1.75
BP70	Transistor Radio Fault-finding Chart	£0.95
BP72	A Microprocessor Primer	£1.75
BP74	Electronic Music Projects	£2.50
BP76	Power Supply Projects	£2.50
BP77	Microprocessing Systems and Circuits (Elements of Electronics — Book 4)	£2.95
BP78	Practical Computer Experiments	£1.75
BP80	Popular Electronic Circuits - Book 1	£2.95
BP84	Digital IC Projects	£1.95
BP85	International Transistor Equivalents Guide	£3.50
BP86	An Introduction to BASIC Programming Techniques	£1.95
BP87	50 Simple LED Circuits — Book 2	£1.35
BP88	How to Use Op-Amps	£2.95
BP89	Communication (Elements of Electronics — Book 5)	£2.95
BP90	Audio Projects	£2.50
BP91	An Introduction to Radio DXing	£1.95
BP92	Electronics Simplified — Crystal Set Construction	£1.75
BP93	Electronic Timer Projects	£1.95
BP94	Electronic Projects for Cars and Boats	£1.95
BP95	Model Railway Projects	£1.95
BP97	IC Projects for Beginners	£1.95
BP98	Popular Electronic Circuits — Book 2	£2.25
BP99	Mini-matrix Board Projects	£2.50
BP101	How to Identify Unmarked ICs	£0.95
BP103	Multi-circuit Board Projects	£1.95
BP104	Electronic Science Projects	£2.95
BP105	Aerial Projects	£1.95
BP106	Modern Op-amp Projects	£1.95
BP107	30 Solderless Breadboard Projects — Book 1	£2.25
BP108	International Diode Equivalents Guide	£2.25
BP109	The Art of Programming the 1K ZX81	£1.95
BP110	How to Get Your Electronic Projects Working	£2.50
BP111	Audio (Elements of Electronics — Book 6)	£3.50
BP112	A Z-80 Workshop Manual	£3.50
BP113	30 Solderless Breadboard Projects — Book 2	£2.25
BP114	The Art of Programming the 16K ZX81	£2.50
BP115	The Pre-computer Book	£1.95
BP117	Practical Electronic Building Blocks — Book 1	£1.95
BP118	Practical Electronic Building Blocks — Book 2	£1.95
BP119	The Art of Programming the ZX Spectrum	£2.50
BP120	Audio Amplifier Fault-finding Chart	£0.95
BP121	How to Design and Make Your Own PCB's	£2.50
BP122	Audio Amplifier Construction	£2.25
BP123	A Practical Introduction to Microprocessors	£2.50
BP124	Easy Add-on Projects for Spectrum, ZX81 & Ace	£2.75
BP125	25 Simple Amateur Band Aerials	£1.95
BP126	BASIC & PASCAL in Parallel	£1.50
BP127	How to Design Electronic Projects	£2.25
BP128	20 Programs for the ZX Spectrum and 16K ZX81	£1.95
BP129	An Introduction to Programming the ORIC-1	£1.95
BP130	Micro Interfacing Circuits — Book 1	£2.25
BP131	Micro Interfacing Circuits — Book 2	£2.75

BP132	25 Simple Shortwave Broadcast Band Aerials	£1.95
BP133	An Introduction to Programming the Dragon 32	£1.95
BP135	Secrets of the Commodore 64	£1.95
BP136	25 Simple Indoor and Window Aerials	£1.75
BP137	BASIC & FORTRAN in Parallel	£1.95
BP138	BASIC & FORTH in Parallel	£1.95
BP139	An Introduction to Programming the BBC Model B Micro	£1.95
BP140	Digital IC Equivalents & Pin Connections	£5.95
BP141	Linear IC Equivalents & Pin Connections	£5.95
BP142	An Introduction to Programming the Acorn Electron	£1.95
BP143	An Introduction to Programming the Atari 600/800XL	£1.95
BP144	Further Practical Electronics Calculations and Formulae	£4.95
BP145	25 Simple Tropical and MW Band Aerials	£1.75
BP146	The Pre-BASIC Book	£2.95
BP147	An Introduction to 6502 Machine Code	£2.50
BP148	Computer Terminology Explained	£1.95
BP149	A Concise Introduction to the Language of BBC BASIC	£1.95
BP152	An Introduction to Z80 Machine Code	£2.75
BP153	An Introduction to Programming the Amstrad CPC464 and 664	£2.50
BP154	An Introduction to MSX BASIC	£2.50
BP156	An Introduction to QL Machine Code	£2.50
BP157	How to Write ZX Spectrum and Spectrum+ Games Programs	£2.50
BP158	An Introduction to Programming the Commodore 16 and Plus 4	£2.50
BP159	How to write Amstrad CPC 464 Games Programs	£2.50
BP161	Into the QL Archive	£2.50
BP162	Counting on QL Abacus	£2.50
BP169	How to Get Your Computer Programs Running	£2.50
BP170	An Introduction to Computer Peripherals	£2.50
BP171	Easy Add-on Projects for Amstrad CPC 464, 664, 6128 and MSX Computers	£3.50
BP173	Computer Music Projects	£2.95
BP174	More Advanced Electronic Music Projects	£2.95
BP175	How to Write Word Game Programs for the Amstrad CPC 464, 664 and 6128	£2.95
BP176	A TV-DXers Handbook	£5.95
BP177	An Introduction to Computer Communications	£2.95
BP179	Electronic Circuits for the Computer Control of Robots	£2.95
BP180	Electronic Circuits for the Computer Control of Model Railways	£2.95
BP181	Getting the Most from Your Printer	£2.95
BP182	MIDI Projects	£2.95
BP183	An Introduction to CP/M	£2.95
BP184	An Introduction to 68000 Assembly Language	£2.95
BP185	Electronic Synthesiser Construction	£2.95
BP186	Walkie-Talkie Projects	£2.95
BP187	A Practical Reference Guide to Word Processing on the Amstrad PCW8256 & PCW8512	£5.95
BP188	Getting Started with BASIC and LOGO on the Amstrad PCWs	£5.95
BP189	Using Your Amstrad CPC Disc Drives	£2.95
BP190	More Advanced Electronic Security Projects	£2.95
BP191	Simple Applications of the Amstrad CPCs for Writers	£2.95
BP192	More Advanced Power Supply Projects	£2.95
BP193	LOGO for Beginners	£2.95
BP194	Modern Opto Device Projects	£2.95
BP195	An Introduction to Satellite Television	£5.95
BP196	BASIC & LOGO in Parallel	£2.95
BP197	An Introduction to the Amstrad PC's	£5.95
BP198	An Introduction to Antenna Theory	£2.95
BP199	An Introduction to BASIC-2 on the Amstrad PC's	£5.95
BP230	An Introduction to GEM	£5.95
BP232	A Concise Introduction to MS-DOS	£2.95
BP233	Electronic Hobbyists Handbook	£4.95
BP234	Transistor Selector Guide	£4.95
BP235	Power Selector Guide	£4.95
BP236	Digital IC Selector Guide-Part 1	£4.95
BP237	Digital IC Selector Guide-Part 2	£4.95
BP238	Linear IC Selector Guide	£4.95
BP239	Getting the Most from Your Multimeter	£2.95
BP240	Remote Control Handbook	£3.95
BP241	An Introduction to 8086 Machine Code	£5.95
BP242	An Introduction to Computer Aided Drawing	£2.95
BP243	BBC BASIC86 on the Amstrad PC's and IBM Compatibles — Book 1: Language	£3.95
BP244	BBC BASIC86 on the Amstrad PC's and IBM Compatibles — Book 2: Graphics & Disc Files	£3.95
BP245	Digital Audio Projects	£2.95
BP246	Musical Applications of the Atari ST's	£4.95
BP247	More Advanced MIDI Projects	£2.95
BP248	Test Equipment Construction	£2.95
BP249	More Advanced Test Equipment Construction	£2.95
BP250	Programming in FORTRAN 77	£4.95
BP251	Computer Hobbyists Handbook	£5.95
BP252	An Introduction to C	£2.95
BP253	Ultra High Power Amplifier Construction	£3.95
BP254	From Atoms to Amperes	£2.95
BP255	International Radio Stations Guide	£4.95
BP256	An Introduction to Loudspeakers and Enclosure Design	£2.95
BP257	An Introduction to Amateur Radio	£2.95
BP258	Learning to Program in C	£4.95